MATHEMATICAL CENTRE TRACTS

1

# FIXED AND ALMOST FIXED POINTS

BY

T. VAN DER WALT



MATHEMATISCH CENTRUM AMSTERDAM

1963

MATHEMATICAL CENTRE TRACTS

1

CONTENTS

# ERRATA

| page | line | |
|---|---|---|
| 9 | 15 | <u>for</u> absolute retract <u>read</u> absolute neighbourhood retract |
| 9 | 26 | <u>for</u> locally topological <u>read</u> locally convex topological |
| 11 | 23 | <u>for</u> theorem to <u>read</u> theorem for the two-cell to |
| 21 | 8 | <u>for</u> [and an AR] <u>read</u> and an absolute retract |
| 23 | 33 | <u>for</u> rest <u>read</u> latter |
| 63 | 8 | <u>for</u> admits <u>read</u> admit |
| 66 | 27 | <u>for</u> continuum <u>read</u> metric continuum |
| 89 | 30 | <u>for</u> [0,1] <u>read</u> [0,1) |
| 94 | 15 | <u>for</u> fixed. <u>read</u> fixed |

Aân my ouers

Aan my vrou

## INTRODUCTION

In 1912 Brouwer [3] proved his by now classical theorem which states that the n-cell C has the fixed point property (f.p.p.) for continuous mappings, i.e. for every continuous mapping $f : C \rightarrow C$ there exists a point $x_o \in C$ such that $f(x_o) = x_o$. This result was extended to compact convex subsets of

(i) certain function spaces, e.g. $L_2[0,1]$ and $C^n[0,1]$, by Birkhoff and Kellogg [1] (1922);

(ii) Banach spaces, by Schauder [1,2] (1927, 1930);

(iii) locally convex topological linear spaces, by Tychonoff [1] (1935).

All these theorems are included in Lefschetz's fixed point theorem (Lefschetz [1] (1926)), or in extensions of it, e.g. Lefschetz [5,6] (1942). From Lefschetz's theorem it follows e.g. that an acyclic compact metric absolute retract has the f.p.p.. Lefschetz [5] (1942) also gave sufficient conditions for the existence of coincidence points under two continuous mappings of one space into another. These results are discussed in section 1 of Chapter I.

The second section of Chapter I is a survey of the Leray-Schauder theory of the local fixed point index (Leray-Schauder [1] (1934)), especially of Browder's extension of this theory (Browder [5] (1960)). Lefschetz's fixed point theorem is in turn contained in the Leray-Schauder theory as extended by Browder.

Brouwer's fixed point theorem for the n-cell was also extended to upper semi-continuous mappings of a compact convex subset of a locally topological linear space into the family of its non-empty closed convex subsets (Kakutani [2] (1941), Bohnenblust and Karlin [1] (1950), Fan [1] (1952) and Glicksberg [1] (1952)). These theorems are included in the extension of Lefschetz's fixed point theorem to upper semi-continuous mappings of a compact lc-space (see p. 43) into the family of its non-empty closed acyclic subsets (Eilenberg and Montgomery [1] (1946), Begle [3] (1950)). In a recent publication Fan [3] (1961) gave sufficient conditions for the existence of coincidence points under upper semi-continuous mappings of a Hausdorff space into the family of non-empty compact convex subsets of a topological linear space. His theorems include Tychonoff's theorem (Tychonoff [1] ), but they do not include the above-mentioned extensions of Tychonoff's theorem, nor are they included in these extensions.

It is unknown whether a compact convex subset of an arbitrary topological linear space has the f.p.p., even when the space is metrizable.

Another unsolved problem bearing on section 7 of Chapter I was referred to by Isbell [1] (1957): If F is a commutative family of continuous mappings of a tree T into itself, does there exist a point $x_0 \in T$ such that $f(x_0) = x_0$ for all $f \in F$?

In Chapter II Scherrer's theorem (Scherrer [1] (1926)), which states that a dendrite has the f.p.p., and its generalizations to a wider class of spaces and mappings are surveyed. An unsolved problem in this field is the question whether a tree-like continuum has the f.p.p. (Bing [2] (1951)). It is also unknown whether a plane continuum which does not separate the plane has the f.p.p.

Chapter III contains miscellaneous fixed point theorems and a general impression is best obtained from the section headings.

If f is a (not necessarily continuous) mapping of a topological space X into itself, and $f(x) \neq x$ for all $x \in X$, then it might be of importance to know whether there exists a point $x_0 \in X$ which in some sense is "near" to its image $f(x_0)$. We would prefer an "almost fixed point property" which can be considered as an extension of the f.p.p. e.g. so that it coincides with f.p.p. in the case of compact spaces and continuous mappings. Existing theorems on almost fixed points are discussed in section 10 of Chapter III, and in Chapter IV we prove the following theorems on almost fixed points in the Euclidean plane.

THEOREM 1. Let $\alpha$ be a finite covering of the Euclidean plane by convex open sets, and let $f : E^2 \longrightarrow E^2$ be continuous. Then there is a member $U \in \alpha$ such that $U \cap f[U] \neq \emptyset$, or equivalently: there exists a point $x_0 \in E^2$ such that $x_0$ and $f(x_0)$ lie in the same member of $\alpha$ .

THEOREM 2. Let $\alpha$ be a finite covering of $E^2$ by arcwise connected sets, and let $f : E^2 \longrightarrow E^2$ be topologically equivalent to an orientation preserving isometry, i.e. there is a homeomorphism h of $E^2$ onto itself and an orientation preserving isometry $g : E^2 \longrightarrow E^2$ such that $f = h^{-1}gh$. Then there exists a member $U \in \alpha$ such that $U \cap f[U] \neq \emptyset$. In particular this is true when $\alpha$ is a finite covering consisting of connected open sets.

THEOREM 3. Let X be a unicoherent topological space and $\alpha$ a covering of X which consists of three connected open sets. Let $f : X \longrightarrow X$ be continuous. Then there exists a member $U \in \alpha$ such that $U \cap f[U] \neq \emptyset$.

An example is given which shows that "orientation preserving" cannot be missed in theorem 2, and that theorem 3 cannot be extended to coverings consisting of more than three sets. The mapping of this example is a transflection, i.e. a reflection followed by a translation in the direction of the axis of reflection, and the covering consists of four connected open sets $\{U_i\}_{i=1}^{4}$ such that $U_i \cap U_j$ $(i \neq j)$ has countably infinitely many components. Note that a transflection reverses the orientation. Thus we have the following

PROBLEM. Let $\alpha$ be a finite open covering of the Euclidean plane $E^2$, and let $f : E^2 \longrightarrow E^2$ be continuous. Does there exist a member $U \in \alpha$ such that $U \cap f[U] \neq \emptyset$ in one or both of the following cases:

(i) f is an orientation preserving homeomorphism onto;

(ii) the intersection of each pair of members of $\alpha$ has at most a finite number of components?

The results of Chapter IV will also be published elsewhere (de Groot, de Vries and van der Walt [1] ).

We did not survey the numerous applications of fixed point theorems. Therefore we mention here a few examples and references. Arnold [1] (1949) used Brouwer's fixed point theorem to obtain an elegant proof of the fundamental theorem of algebra. In a description of a model of the brain, Zeeman [1] (1962) gave an interesting application of Brouwer's fixed point theorem for the n-cell. For expositions of applications to functional analysis, the reader is referred to Graves [1] (1935), Nemyčkiĭ [1] (1936), Rothe [5] (1939), Miranda [1] (1949), Leray [5] (1950) and Fuller [3] (1962); for more detailed results, see e.g. Kyner [1,2] (1956, 1958), Marcus [1,2] (1956), Browder [6] (1957), Stokes [1] (1960) and Cesari [1] (1960).

I wish to express my gratitude to Professor J. de Groot who suggested this study, in particular the problems which are discussed in Chapter IV. I am grateful to the Potchefstroom University for C.H.E. and the University of Amsterdam, at both of which institutions I studied for several years. I am indebted to Professor R.D. Anderson and Professor V.L. Klee for valuable remarks. I wish to thank the Potchefstroom University for C.H.E. and the South African Council for Scientific and Industrial Research, from both of whom I received bursaries during my stay in Amsterdam. I am grateful to the Mathematical Centre, Amsterdam, for the privilege of being appointed a guest member of their staff, and for the most helpful cooperation that I received from them.

## CONVENTIONS AND DEFINITIONS

The empty set will be denoted by $\emptyset$. If X and Y are sets, and every element of X is an element of Y, we shall write $X \subset Y$. It will be explicitly stated whenever X is meant to be a <u>proper</u> subset of Y. If X and Y are sets, then the set of all points of X which do not belong to Y is denoted by $X \setminus Y$.

A <u>neighbourhood</u> of a point [subset] of a topological space is an <u>open</u> set containing the point [subset]. If A is a subset of a metric space X with metric $\rho$, and $\varepsilon$ is a positive number, then $\{x \in X |$ there exists a point $a \in A$ such that $\rho(x,a) < \varepsilon\}$ will be denoted by $U_\varepsilon(A)$. If A is a subset of a topological space X, then $\overline{A}$ will denote the <u>closure</u> of A in X. A topological space will be called <u>compact</u> if every open covering of it has a finite subcovering. A compact metric space is called a <u>compactum</u>.

A <u>continuum</u> is a compact connected Hausdorff space. A continuum is <u>decomposable</u> if it is the union of two proper subcontinua; otherwise it is indecomposable. A connected topological space X is <u>unicoherent</u> if, whenever $X = A \cup B$, $A \neq \emptyset$, $B \neq \emptyset$, with both A and B connected and closed in X, it follows that $A \cap B$ is connected. A continuum is <u>hereditarily decomposable</u> [<u>indecomposable</u>, <u>unicoherent</u>] if each of its non-degenerate subcontinua is decomposable [indecomposable, unicoherent].

A <u>Peano continuum</u> is a Hausdorff space which is the continuous image of the closed interval [0,1] (with the usual topology). It is well-known that the class of Peano continua coincides with the class of locally connected metric continua, and that a Peano continuum is arcwise connected.

A <u>dendrite</u> is a Peano continuum which contains no Jordan curve. If A,B and C are three mutually disjoint subsets of a topological space X, then C <u>separates</u> A and B in X if $X \setminus C$ can be split into two disjoint sets, each of which is closed in $X \setminus C$, and respectively contains A and B. A <u>tree</u> is a continuum in which each pair of distinct points is separated by a third point. In this terminology, a dendrite is a metric tree (Whyburn [1, p.88]). A continuum is a tree if and only if it is locally connected and hereditarily unicoherent (Ward [2]).

The terms mapping, function and transformation will be used synonymously, and a mapping f of a set X into a set Y will be denoted by $f : X \to Y$. Further, if $A \subset X$ and $B \subset Y$, then $f[A] = \{f(a) \mid a \in A\}$, $f^{-1}[B] = \{x \in X \mid f(x) \in B\}$.

Let X and Y be topological spaces, and let $\mathcal{A}(Y)$ denote the family of all non-empty subsets of Y. The upper semi-finite (u.s.f.) topology for $\mathcal{A}(Y)$ has as a basis for its open sets all sets of the form $\{A \in \mathcal{A}(Y) \mid A \subset U\}$, where U is an open subset of Y. The lower semi-finite (l.s.f.) topology has as a basis for its open sets all sets of the form $\{A \in \mathcal{A}(Y) \mid A \cap U \neq \emptyset\}$. The finite topology for $\mathcal{A}(Y)$ has as a subbasis the sets $\{A \in \mathcal{A}(Y) \mid A \subset U,\ A \cap V \neq \emptyset\}$, with U and V open in Y.

A mapping $f : X \to \mathcal{A}(Y)$ is called upper semi-continuous (u.s.c.) [lower semi-continuous (l.s.c.), continuous] if and only if it is continuous in the usual sense with respect to the upper semi-finite [lower semi-finite, finite] topology for $\mathcal{A}(Y)$. This means that f is continuous if and only if it is both u.s.c. and l.s.c., and that f is u.s.c. [l.s.c.] if and only if, for each point $x \in X$ and for each open set U of Y containing f(x) [such that $f(x) \cap U \neq \emptyset$], there exists a neighbourhood V of x such that $f(z) \subset U$ [$f(z) \cap U \neq \emptyset$] for all $z \in V$.

If $\mathcal{S}(Y)$ is a subfamily of $\mathcal{A}(Y)$, a mapping $f : X \to \mathcal{S}(Y)$ is called u.s.c. [l.s.c., continuous] if it is continuous with respect to the relative topology for $\mathcal{S}(Y)$ induced by $\mathcal{A}(Y)$ endowed with the u.s.f. [l.s.f., finite] topology.

Various other definitions of upper and lower semi-continuity exist (see e.g. Strother [1] and the references given there), but they are nearly all equivalent when X and Y are compact Hausdorff spaces and $\mathcal{S}(Y)$ is the family of all non-empty closed subsets of Y.

A mapping $f : X \to \mathcal{S}(Y)$ is also called a multi-valued or a set-valued mapping; for instance, if $\mathcal{S}(Y)$ is the family of all non-empty closed subsets of Y, then f is referred to as a "closed set-valued mapping". Occasionally it will then be convenient to refer to a mapping $g : X \to Y$ as "single-valued".

If $A \subset X$, $B \subset Y$, then $f[A] = \bigcup\{f(x) \mid x \in A\}$, $f^{-1}[B] = \{x \in X \mid f(x) \cap B \neq \emptyset\}$, and the graph G(f) of f is defined to be $\{(x,y) \mid x \in X,\ y \in Y,\ y \in f(x)\}$. Thus f[A] and G(f) are defined as subsets of Y and $X \times Y$ respectively, and not of $\mathcal{S}(Y)$ and $X \times \mathcal{S}(Y)$.

Let X and Y be sets and let $\mathcal{S}(X)$ and $\mathcal{T}(Y)$ denote families of non-empty subsets respectively of X and Y. Let $f : X \rightarrow \mathcal{T}(Y)$ and $g : Y \rightarrow \mathcal{S}(X)$ be mappings. A coincidence point of X and Y under f and g is a point $(x_0, y_0) \in X \times Y$ such that $x_0 \in g(y_0)$ and $y_0 \in f(x_0)$. We may also consider mappings $f : X \rightarrow \mathcal{T}(Y)$, $g : X \rightarrow \mathcal{S}(Y)$, defined in the same direction. Then a coincidence point of X under f and g is a point $x_0 \in X$ such that $f(x_0) \cap g(x_0) \neq \emptyset$. In the special case when $Y = X$ and g is defined by $g(x) = \{x\}$ for all $x \in X$, $x_0$ is called a fixed point of X under f. If $\mathcal{F}$ is a family of functions, each of which is on X to the same family $\mathcal{S}(X)$ of subsets of X, and if X has a fixed point under each member $f \in \mathcal{F}$, then X is said to have the fixed point property (f.p.p.) for the family $\mathcal{F}$.

If $x_0$ is a fixed point of X under $f : X \rightarrow \mathcal{S}(X)$, we shall also say that the mapping f has a fixed point in X; also, that $x_0$ is an f-invariant point.

For the sake of completeness, we note that a mapping $f : X \rightarrow Y$ induces a mapping $f^* : X \rightarrow \mathcal{O}(Y) = \{\{y\} \mid y \in Y\}$ in the obvious way, and by a fixed point of X under f we shall mean a fixed point of X under $f^*$. An analogous remark applies to coincidence points.

A topological space X will be said to lack the f.p.p. if there exists a continuous mapping $f : X \rightarrow X$ such that $f(x) \neq x$ for all $x \in X$.

Let X be a Hausdorff space and H a homology theory for X over a group G. Then X is called acyclic (with respect to G) if the homology groups $H_n(X,G)$ $(n=0,1,2,\ldots)$ are trivial, $H_0(X,G)$ being taken augmented. A continuum is hereditarily acyclic if each of its subcontinua is acyclic.

A topological space X is an absolute retract [absolute neighbourhood retract] if, for each normal space Y and each closed subset X' of Y which is homeomorphic to X, X' is a retract [neighbourhood retract] of Y. A necessary and sufficient condition for a compact metric space to be an absolute retract [absolute neighbourhood retract] is that it possesses a topological image in the Hilbert cube $I^\omega$ which is a retract [neighbourhood retract] of $I^\omega$. (Borsuk [1]). A compact metric absolute retract [absolute neighbourhood retract] will be denoted by AR [ANR], and a space which is homeomorphic to a retract [neighbourhood retract] of a Tychonoff cube $I^A$ by $AR^*$ [$ANR^*$].

Euclidean n-space will always be denoted by $E^n$, and the n-sphere in $E^{n+1}$ by $S^n$.

The topological structure of the topological groups and topological linear spaces to be considered will be Hausdorff, and the linear spaces will be real.

For other terms in general topology, homology theory and linear analysis, the reader is referred to Alexandroff-Hopf [1] , Dunford and Schwartz [1] , Eilenberg and Steenrod [1] , Kelley [4], Kuratowski [1] , Lefschetz [5,6,7] , Whyburn [1] and Wilder [1] .

# CHAPTER I

## The fixed point theorems of Brouwer, Lefschetz, Schauder, Leray, Tychonoff and Kakutani

### 1.1. Single-valued mappings

In one of a series of papers on curves defined by differential equations, Poincaré [1] (1885) considered a continuous vector field over a closed surface and assigned an integer as index to each isolated singular point. He proved that if the surface is orientable and of genus $\neq 1$, then there exists at least one singular point.

Around 1910 Brouwer [1-3] discovered the degree of a continuous mapping of one n-manifold into another. He used it to extend Poincaré's definition of the index from two to n dimensions, and to prove his well-known fixed point theorems for the n-cell, the n-sphere and the projective plane:

B1. The n-cell has the f.p.p. for continuous mappings.

B2. The n-sphere has the f.p.p. for continuous mappings of degree $\neq (-1)^n$.

B3. The projective plane has the f.p.p. for continuous mappings.

In 1922 Alexander [1] gave new proofs of B1 and B2, under the impression that they were proved for homeomorphisms only. He also extended B3 to projective 2n-space. Almost simultaneously Birkhoff and Kellogg [1] (1922), under the same impression as Alexander, gave another proof of B1, and showed that it may be extended to special function spaces, namely to compact convex subsets of $C^n[0,1]$ and $L_2[0,1]$. (See Dunford and Schwartz [1] for definitions.) A short and elegant proof of B1 was given by Knaster, Kuratowski and Mazurkiewicz [1] (1929).

Another major step in the history of fixed point theorems was the formula of Lefschetz [1] (1926). Let f be a continuous mapping of an orientable n-manifold M, without boundary, into itself. Let $\bar{z}_r^i$ ($i=1,2,\dots,p_r$; $r=0,1,\dots,n$) be a basis of the r-th homology group $H_r(M)$ of M, taken over the rationals as coefficients, and let

$$f_{*r}(\bar{z}_r^i) = \sum_{j=1}^{p_r} a_{ij}^r \ \bar{z}_r^j \quad (i=1,2,\dots,p_r),$$

where $f_{*r}$ denotes the homomorphism of $H_r(M)$ into itself induced by f, and the $a_{ij}^r$ are rational numbers. Let trace $f_{*r} = \sum_{i=1}^{p_r} a_{ii}^r$, and $\Lambda(f) = \sum_{r=0}^{n} (-1)^r$ trace $f_{*r}$.

Lefschetz's theorem now asserts that $\Lambda(f) \neq 0$ is a sufficient condition for the existence of fixed points of M under f.

Lefschetz [2] (1927) almost immediately generalized this result to manifolds with a boundary. It was then extended to finite polyhedra by Hopf [1] (1929), and again by Lefschetz [4] (1937) to the AR's and ANR's, and eventually also to the HLC*-spaces and the quasi-complexes (Lefschetz [5] (1942)). Lefschetz also obtained analogous formulas giving sufficient conditions for the existence of coincidence points of manifolds under continuous mappings. A full account of these results is given in Lefschetz [5,6].

Each of the spaces considered above is a compact Hausdorff space, with all its rational Betti numbers finite and all but a finite number of them zero. From the extended Lefschetz formula it follows, for example, that every ANR which is acyclic over the group of rational numbers, has the f.p.p. for continuous mappings. The property of being acyclic alone is not enough to ensure the existence of fixed points, as was shown by Borsuk [5] (1935) who constructed an acyclic Peano continuum in $E^3$ which can be mapped topologically onto itself without fixed points. Verčenko [1] (1940) constructed a 3-dimensional continuum in $E^4$ which has the properties of the space in Borsuk's example and in addition is simply connected. On the other hand, it has been proved by Cartwright and Littlewood [1] (1951) that if a topological mapping of a plane acyclic continuum X can be extended to a homeomorphism of the whole plane, then X must have fixed points under such a mapping. The mapping in the example of Borsuk [5] can be extended to a homeomorphism of $E^3$, so that this additional condition is insufficient to ensure the validity of the theorem in three dimensions.

The fixed point formula of Lefschetz [1] (1926) included almost all the fixed point theorems existing at the time of its publication, e.g., the above mentioned results of Brouwer [1-3].

There are, however, fixed point theorems which escape the formula and its extensions, e.g., the Poincaré-Birkhoff-theorem (G.D. Birkhoff [1] (1912)). This theorem states that if f is a homeomorphism of a plane annular ring bounded by two concentric circles $C_1$ and $C_2$, which moves all the points of $C_1$ in one direction and all those of $C_2$ in the opposite direction, then either some Jordan curve J exists in the ring surrounding the circle $C_1$ which does not meet its image $f[J]$, or else there are exactly two fixed points, and this in spite of the fact that $\Lambda(f) = 0$ here (Lefschetz [7,p.16]). (For extensions of the Poincaré-Birkhoff-theorem, see G.D. Birkhoff [2] (1931) and Rey Pastor [1] (1945).)

In contrast to the homology arguments used in establishing the Lefschetz fixed point formula, various authors used convexity arguments to extend the Brouwer fixed point theorem for the n-cell to compact convex subsets of linear spaces. Thus, in 1927 Schauder [1] extended the results of Birkhoff and Kellogg [1] to metric topological linear spaces having a linear base. This assumption was then dropped, and in 1930 Schauder [2] obtained the following results:

S1. A compact convex subset of a Banach space has the f.p.p. for continuous mappings.

S2. A convex, weakly compact subset of a separable Banach space has the f.p.p. for weakly continuous mappings.

A result of Mazur [1] (1930) states that the convex closure of a compact subset of a Banach space is compact. Krein and Šmulian [1] (1940) extended this result by showing that the convex closure of a weakly compact subset of a Banach space is weakly compact, and they used it to establish the following improved form of S2:

S2a. If H is a closed convex subset of a Banach space, and $f : H \longrightarrow H$ is weakly continuous such that $f[H]$ is separable and the weak closure of $f[H]$ is weakly compact, then H has a fixed point under f.

Let X be a Banach space. With the assumption of Mazur's theorem mentioned above, theorem S1 may be stated in any one of the following three equivalent forms:

S1a. If $f : X \to X$ is continuous and such that $f[X]$ is bounded, and the image of each bounded set has a compact closure, then X has a fixed point under f.

S1b. If H is a closed convex subset of X and $f : X \to X$ is continuous and such that $\overline{f[H]}$ is compact, then H has a fixed point under f.

S1c. If H is a compact convex subset of X and $f : H \to H$ is continuous, then H has a fixed point under f.

S1c and S1b was extended to locally convex topological linear spaces by Tychonoff [1] (1935) and Hukuhara [1] (1950) respectively. Using the fixed point formula for ANR's (Lefschetz [5]), Browder [3] (1959) obtained the following extensions of S1a and S1b, in which the hypothesis about the mapping is replaced by a corresponding hypothesis about one of the iterates of the mapping:

S1a'. If $f : X \to X$ is continuous and such that for some positive integer m the set $f^m[X]$ is bounded, and the image of each bounded set has a compact closure, then X has a fixed point under f.

S1b'. Let H and $H_1$ be open convex subsets of X, $H_0$ a closed convex subset of X, $H_0 \subset H_1 \subset H$, $f : H \to X$ continuous and such that $\overline{f[H]}$ is compact. Suppose that for a positive integer m, $f^m$ is well-defined on $H_1$, $\bigcup_{i=0}^{m} f^i [H_0] \subset H_1$, while $f^m[H_1] \subset H_0$. Then $H_0$ has a fixed point under f.

Browder [3] observed that the methods applied in the proofs generalize directly to locally convex topological linear spaces and give extensions of Tychonoff's generalization of Schauder's theorem to locally convex spaces. The following interesting consequence of the Lefschetz fixed point theorem is stated for comparison with form S1c of Schauder's theorem (Browder [3]):

Let A be an ANR, or a quasi-complex in the sense of Lefschetz [5] . Let $f : A \to A$ be continuous and suppose that for some positive integer m, $f^m[A]$ is contained in a closed acyclic subset B of A. Then A has a fixed point under f.

We conclude this section with the remark that it is not known whether a compact convex subset of an arbitrary topological linear space has the f.p.p., not even when the space is metrizable (Klee [6 , p.285; 7, p.291]), and that Lefschetz's proof for the assertion that a compact convex subset of a metric linear space has the f.p.p. ( Lefschetz [6, p.119] ) is in error,[1] as was pointed out by Klee [9] .

If H is a compact convex subset of a metric linear space X, then (Klee [6] ):

(i) H is a compact subset of a metric space X;
(ii) every neighbourhood of H in X contains an open [and also a closed] neighbourhood which is contractible, locally contractible [and an AR] ;
(iii) H is contractible;
(iv) H is locally contractible.

An example of Borsuk [6] (1948) shows that a space may satisfy all four conditions without being an AR. Kinoshita [2] (1953) constructed a space which satisfies (i), (ii) and (iii) but lacks the f.p.p. It seems to be unknown whether the f.p.p. for H follows from (i), (ii) and (iv), or from (i), (iii) and (iv). However, if a space satisfies (i), (iii) and (iv), and in addition is finite-dimensional, then Lefschetz's proof (Lefschetz [6, p.119]) is in order (Klee [9] ); such a space then is an AR and hence has the f.p.p. for continuous mappings.

For arbitrary topological linear spaces, we have the following result (Klee [7] ):

Let X be a topological linear space and H a compact retract of X which admits arbitrary small continuous displacements into finite dimensional subspaces of X, i.e., for each neighbourhood U of the origin in X there is a finite-dimensional subspace L of X and a continuous mapping $g : H \longrightarrow L$ such that $g[H]$ is compact and $g[H] \subset H + U$.

Then H has the f.p.p. for continuous mappings.

## 1.2. <u>The Leray-Schauder theory of the fixed point index and its extensions</u>

Except for minor changes, this section is taken verbally from Browder [5] (1960).

In the classical fixed point theory of continuous mappings, culminating in the Lefschetz fixed point theorem (Lefschetz [1,2]), one is concerned with the algebraic number of fixed points of a

---

[1] However, see the remark preceding the last theorem of this section.

continuous mapping f of a compact, locally well-behaved space X into itself. Beginning with the work of Leray and Schauder [1] and Leray [1] in 1934 on the local degree for completely continuous displacements[1] in a Banach space, the problem has arisen of localizing this index of fixed points, i.e. of defining an algebraic measure of the number of fixed points of the mapping f on each open subset of X whose boundary does not intersect the fixed point set and of doing so in a way which preserves the principal properties that make such a measure useful in the growing number of applications which the fixed point theory has found in analysis.

The principal results in this direction are to be found in the papers of Leray [2,3,4], written during the Second World War and published shortly afterwards, in which he constructed a theory of the fixed point index for continuous mappings of convexoid spaces, a class of spaces sharing some of the properties of finite polytopes and of finite unions of compact convex sets in linear spaces. Their precise definition is the following:

A compact topological space X is said to be <u>convexoid</u> if it has a covering $\{U_\xi\}$ having the following properties (Leray [2,3,4]):

(a) Each $U_\xi$ is closed and acyclic (with respect to Čech cohomology theory).

(b) The intersection of any finite number of the $U_\xi$ lies in the collection if it is non-empty.

(c) Each point of X possesses arbitrarily small neighbourhoods each of which is the union of a finite number of the sets $U_\xi$.

Leray's theory in its initial form, though definitive for the class of spaces which he treats, suffers from the disadvantage that the class of convexoid spaces fits in poorly with the usual classification of topological spaces by their local regularity properties (i.e. local n-connectedness in the sense of homology or homotopy). In a sense, the requirement that a space be convexoid is a condition analogous to triangulability for a manifold, since

-------------

1) Let X be a Banach space, A a subset of X and i : A ⟶ A the identity mapping. A mapping f : A ⟶ A is a completely continuous displacement if f is continuous and (i-f) [A] has a compact closure in X.

it requires that one should be able to build up the space by pasting together regular pieces (no longer simplexes, but cohomologically trivial sets) in such a fashion that their intersections should also be regular. The difficulty can be illustrated by the fact that it is not clear whether an Euclidean manifold (i.e. one without differentiability or triangulability conditions) is convexoid.

Motivated by the desire to construct a theory of the fixed point index in a context similar to that in which Lefschetz [5] has proved his fixed point theorem, Browder [1] (1948) in his Princeton Doctoral thesis (written under the joint sponsorship of Lefschetz and Hurewicz), established a theory of the fixed point index for ANR*'s using as a tool Leray's theory as applied to finite polytopes. (See also Browder [2] ).) The results and the general philosophy of Browder [1] are summarized by Bourgin [1, p.229-235] . In his M.I.T. Doctoral thesis of 1953 (written under Hurewicz), O'Neill [1] rederived the principal results of Leray's theory for the special case of finite polytopes. Using the results of O'Neill's paper, Bourgin [2] (1955) has recently reestablished the theory of the fixed point index for ANR*'s, along lines similar to those of Browder [1] .

Leray [5] (1950) pointed out the possibility of extending his theory from convexoid spaces to retracts of convexoid spaces (which include the ANR*'s. Such an extension has recently been carried through in detail by Deleanu [3] (1959) who also applies some sharpened forms of Leray's results given by Leray [6] (1959).

The theory of the local fixed point index, as initiated by Leray-Schauder [1] (1934) and developed amongst others by Leray [5] (1950), Nagumo [2] (1951) and Altman [2,3] (1958) is applicable to <u>locally convex</u> topological linear spaces. For Banach spaces, a homotopy extension theorem of Granas [1] (1959) yields many of the useful conclusions of the Leray-Schauder theory while avoiding the more complicated notions of the rest. Klee [7] (1960) showed that it is possible to expand to an arbitrary topological linear space both the Leray-Schauder theory and the homotopy extension approach of Granas.

Browder's objective (Browder [5]) is to go outside the frame of reference of ANR*'s or of retraction properties in general, and to take up the theory of the fixed point index on the combinatorial or homology level on which it is treated by Leray [4] but under more general hypotheses, similar in their nature to (though not identical with) hypotheses made by Lefschetz [5,p.322-327] in his treatment of the Lefschetz fixed point theorem for the class of quasi-complexes. Intuitively, one should expect that the fixed point index, or algebraic number of fixed points, as the latter name implies, should be a combinatorial or homology concept defined in a class of spaces which are defined by combinatorial restrictions rather than by restrictions upon continuous mappings. Basically, as in the case of finite polytopes treated in the last chapters of Alexandroff-Hopf [1] , his idea is to identify the fixed point index with a count of the number of times some sort of element is mapped back on itself by the given mapping f. He obtains such a count in a very natural form, namely the alternating sum of the traces of induced chain mappings of nerves of X. The general approach goes back to Lefschetz [5] . Browder's proof was announced in Browder [2] (1951). The basic problem is to find the appropriate algebraic analogues of the properties of the fixed point index for chain mappings into a differential graded module G of a differential graded submodule F.

Browder [5] introduces an axiomatic fixed point index in the following way: We are given a category of compact topological spaces X and of permissible continuous mappings $h : X \longrightarrow X$. By a <u>fixed point index</u> on this category the following is meant: if X is a space in the category, O an open subset of X, f any continuous mapping of $\bar{O}$ into X, then if f has no fixed points on $\bar{O}\backslash O$, an integer i (f,O) is defined having the following four properties:

(a) If $f_t$, $0 \leq t \leq 1$, is a homotopy of $f_o$ to $f_1$, where all the $f_t$ are mappings of $\bar{O}$ into X and none have any fixed points on $\bar{O}\backslash O$, then $i\ (f_o,O) = i\ (f_1,O)$. (Invariance under homotopy.)

(b) If O contains a finite family of mutually disjoint open sets $O_j$ ($j=1,2,\ldots,s$) and if $\bar{O} \setminus \bigcup_{j=1}^{s} O_j$ contains no fixed points of the mapping $f : \bar{O} \longrightarrow X$, then

$$i\ (f,O) = \sum_{j=1}^{s} i\ (f,O_j)$$

where each of the summands on the right denotes the index of the restricted mapping $f|\bar{O}_j$. In particular, if $\bar{O}$ itself contains no fixed points of f, then i (f,O) = 0. (Additivity of the index.)

(c) If O = X, then i (f,O) = $\Lambda(f)$, the Lefschetz number of f, where $\Lambda(f) = \sum_{r \geq 0} (-1)^r$ trace $(f_{*r})$, and $f_{*r}$ is the endomorphism of $H_r(X)$ induced by f. ($H_r(X)$ is the r-th dimensional Čech homology group of X with rational coefficients.) In particular, (unless we adopt a generalized definition of trace as in Leray [6] ), one must assume that X has finitely generated homology groups, all but a finite number of which are trivial. (Normalization).

(d) Let $X_1$ and $X_2$ be two spaces of the category, h a permissible mapping of $X_1$ into $X_2$, $O_2$ an open subset of $X_2$, f a continuous mapping of $\bar{O}_2$ into $X_1$. Let $O_1 = h^{-1}[O_2]$ . Suppose that hf has no fixed points on $\bar{O}_2 \setminus O_2$. Then

$$i\ (hf, O_2) = i\ (fh, O_1).$$

(Commutativity).

The property (d) includes as a special case, the following:

(d') Suppose X and X' are members of the category and $X \subset X'$ and the injection mapping $j : X' \longrightarrow X$ is permissible. Let O be an open subset of X, $f : \bar{O} \longrightarrow X$ a continuous mapping such that $f[O] \subset X'$. Suppose f has no fixed points on $\bar{O} \setminus O$. Then

$$i\ (f, O) = i\ (f, X' \cap O).$$

Browder [5] proceeds to establish the existence of a fixed point index for more general categories than the ANR*'s. The categories which he considers are subcategories of the categories of semi-complexes and semi-complex mappings. One such includes all HLC* spaces in the sense of Lefschetz [5] , and all their continuous mappings. The definition of a semi-complex is motivated by deriving its properties from well-known properties of ANR's (Lefschetz [6]). Unlike the latter, however, the structure of this class of spaces is restricted by conditions on chain mappings and not on continuous mappings.

DEFINITIONS (Browder [5] ): Let X be a compact, locally connected Hausdorff space, and let $\Omega$ be the family of all finite open coverings of X. For $\alpha, \beta \in \Omega$, write $\beta > \alpha$ if $\beta$ is a refinement of $\alpha$. For $\alpha \in \Omega$, let $N_\alpha$ be the nerve of $\alpha$ , and $C_n(N_\alpha)$ the vector space of oriented n-chains with rational coefficients.

The support of a simplex $\sigma \in N_\alpha$, Sup($\sigma$), is defined to be the union of the closures of the open sets of $\sigma$ which are vertices of $\sigma$. The support of a chain $g \in C_n(N_\alpha)$, Sup(g), is defined to be the union of the supports of those simplexes of $N_\alpha$ which have non-null coefficients in the expansion of g.

Let $C(N_\alpha)$ be the differential graded module of oriented chains of $N_\alpha$ with rational coefficients, let $d_\alpha$ be the differential of $C(N_\alpha)$, which is of degree (-1). In the following definition, by a chain mapping of $C(N_\alpha)$ into $C(N_\beta)$ is meant a graded homomorphism h of degree zero over the rationals for which, as usual, $d_\beta h = h d_\alpha$, but in addition, it is also assumed that h carries integral chains of $N_\beta$ into integral chains of $N_\alpha$. Two chain mappings h and $h_1$ of $C(N_\alpha)$ into $C(N_\beta)$ are chain homotopic with chain homotopy D if D is a graded homomorphism of $C(N_\alpha)$ into $C(N_\beta)$ of degree (+1) such that $h-h_1 = d_\beta D + D d_\alpha$.

Let X be a compact, locally connected Hausdorff space. X is said to be a semi-complex if there is a semi-complex structure defined on X, where by the latter is meant the following: $(A)_1$ For each $\lambda \in \Omega$ there exists $\alpha_0(\lambda) \in \Omega$ and a family $C_\lambda = \{c_{\alpha\beta}\}$ of one or more chain mappings $c_{\alpha\beta} : C_n(N_\beta) \to C_n(N_\alpha)$ for $\alpha > \beta > \alpha_0(\lambda)$ and all $n \geq 0$, such that the following properties hold for these chain mappings:

(i) If for $\beta, \xi \in \Omega$, with $\beta > \xi$, $j_{\xi\beta}$ is the chain mapping of $C_n(N_\beta)$ into $C_n(N_\xi)$ induced by one of the natural injections of $N_\xi$ into $N_\beta$, then for every $\alpha > \beta > \xi > \alpha_0(\lambda)$, the chain mapping $c_{\alpha\beta}$ is chain homotopic to $c_{\alpha\xi}\ j_{\xi\beta}$ with a chain homotopy small of order $\lambda$, i.e. with a chain homotopy $D^{(1)}_{\alpha\beta}$ such that for every simplex $\sigma \in N_\beta$ and the corresponding elementary n-chain g with coefficient 1,

$$\mathrm{Sup}(g) \cup \mathrm{Sup}(c_{\alpha\beta}(g)) \cup \mathrm{Sup}(D^{(1)}_{\alpha\beta}(g))$$

is contained in a single element of $\lambda$.

(ii) For $\xi > \alpha > \beta > \alpha_0(\lambda)$ the chain mapping $c_{\alpha\beta}$ is chain homotopic to $j_{\alpha\xi}\ c_{\xi\beta}$ with a chain homotopy $D^{(2)}_{\alpha\beta}$ such that

$$\mathrm{Sup}(g) \cup \mathrm{Sup}(c_{\alpha\beta}(g)) \cup \mathrm{Sup}(D^{(2)}_{\alpha\beta}(g))$$

is contained in a single element of $\lambda$ for each elementary n-chain g of $N_\beta$.

(iii) If $\beta > \xi > \alpha_0(\lambda)$, then for every $n \geq 0$ the chain mapping $c_{\beta\xi}\ j_{\xi\beta}$ induces an endomorphism of $H_n(N_\beta)$ which is idempotent and whose image is the submodule of $H_n(N_\beta)$ consisting of coordinates of elements of $H_n(X)$.

(iv) If $\lambda' > \lambda$, then $\alpha_0(\lambda') > \alpha_0(\lambda)$ and $C_{\lambda'}$ is a subfamily of $C_\lambda$.

The most important differences between the definitions of the quasi-complexes (Lefschetz [5, p.323]) and the semi-complexes can be summarized in order of increasing importance as follows (Browder [5, p.269]):

(1) In the definition of the semi-complexes much more detailed restrictions are assumed for the chain mappings $c_{\alpha\beta}$ (which Lefschetz calls chain derivations) than in the definition of a quasi-complex, where for example the chain mappings $c_{\alpha\beta}$ are assumed homologous (which for rational coefficients is equivalent to being chain homotopic) while here it is assumed that they are chain homotopic with small chain homotopies.

(2) In a quasi-complex, condition (iii) is replaced by the stronger condition that $c_{\beta\xi}\ j_{\xi\beta}$ (at least for a cofinal subset of $\beta$ and $\xi$) induces an <u>isomorphism</u> of $H_n(N_\beta)$ onto itself. It follows immediately from this (as was first noted by Dyer [1]) that a quasi-complex has isomorphic homology groups with the nerve of any sufficiently fine covering $\beta$. Consequently it is unclear (despite the statement in Lefschetz [5, p.322]) that the class of quasi-complexes does include the class of ANR's or the more general class of compact spaces which are uniformly locally connected in all dimensions in the sense of homology, the HLC* spaces of Lefschetz. (See for the last, Lefschetz [5], Wilder [1]). On the other hand, the axioms for the semi-complexes are rather obviously satisfied by the HLC* spaces.

<u>Definition of the fixed point index</u> (Browder [5, p.277]).

Let X be a compact Hausdorff space which is a semi-complex. Let O be an open subset of X. Suppose we are given a continuous mapping $f : \bar{O} \rightarrow X$ without any fixed points on $\bar{O} \setminus O$.

Let $\alpha \in \Omega$. We construct a closed sub-polytope $N'_\alpha$ of $N_\alpha$ corresponding to the open set O, where $N'_\alpha$ is the smallest closed sub-polytope of $N_\alpha$ containing all the vertices of $N_\alpha$ which correspond to elements $U_i$ of $\alpha$ which are contained in O. The boundary $N''_\alpha$ of $N'_\alpha$

in the simplicial complex $N_\alpha$ consists of the smallest closed subcomplex of $N'_\alpha$ spanned by vertices corresponding to elements U of $\alpha$ such that there exists $U_1 \in \alpha$ with $U \cap U_1 \neq \emptyset$ and $U_1 \cap (X \setminus O) \neq \emptyset$. The "bounding edge" $N^{(0)}$ of $N'_\alpha$ in $N_\alpha$ is the star of $N''_\alpha$ in $N_\alpha \setminus N'_\alpha$.

Let $\beta \in \Omega$, and let $f^{-1}(\beta) = \{f^{-1}[U] \mid U \in \beta\}$. For each $\alpha > f^{-1}(\beta)$, we define a family of simplicial mappings of $N'_\alpha$ into $N_\beta$ in the following way: For each vertex $q_U$ of $N'_\alpha$, let $f_{\beta\alpha}(q_U) = q_{V(\beta)}$, where the latter is the vertex in $N_\beta$ corresponding to some element $V \in \beta$ for which $f[U] \subset V$. By a standard argument $f_{\beta\alpha}$ can be extended to a simplicial mapping of $N'_\alpha$ into $N_\beta$ and any two such mappings are contiguous in $N_\beta$ and hence homotopic with homotopy paths lying in simplexes of $N_\beta$.

Let $q_\alpha$ denote the standard projection of $C(N_\alpha)$ onto $C(N'_\alpha)$, and let $f_{\beta\alpha}$ also denote the anti-chain mapping obtained from the simplicial mapping $f_{\beta\alpha}$, as follows: For each elementary chain $g_0$ of $C(N'_\alpha)$ corresponding to an n-simplex $\sigma$, we set

$$f_{\beta\alpha}(g_0) = \begin{cases} 0 \text{ if } f(\sigma) \text{ has dimension less than } n \\ (-1)^n g_{f(\sigma)}, \text{ if } f(\sigma) \text{ has dimension } n, \end{cases}$$

where $g_{f(\sigma)}$ is the elementary chain in $C(N_\beta)$ corresponding to the n-simplex $f(\sigma)$. We extend the homomorphism $f_{\beta\alpha}$ by linearity, and the result is trivially an anti-chain mapping.

THEOREM (Browder [5, p.278]). Let $\lambda \in \Omega$, with $\lambda$ composed of connected open sets V. Consider the family of mappings $c_{\alpha\beta}$ in $C_\lambda$ satisfying the conditions $(A)_1$ (p.26). Let $\alpha > \beta > \alpha_0(\lambda)$, $\alpha > f^{-1}(\beta)$. We define

$$i_{\alpha\beta}(f,O) = \text{trace}\,(q_\alpha\, c_{\alpha\beta}\, f_{\beta\alpha}).$$

Then $i_{\alpha\beta}(f,O)$ is the same for all choices of $\alpha$, $\beta$, $c_{\alpha\beta}$ and $f_{\beta\alpha}$, with $\alpha > \beta > \alpha_0(\lambda)$, $\alpha > f^{-1}(\beta)$. This common value is denoted by $i(f,O)$. It is independent of $\lambda$ and $\alpha_0(\lambda)$, for $\lambda$ sufficiently fine.

The fixed point index $i(f,O)$ as defined above depends upon a given structure of a semi-complex on X, i.e. a system of chain mappings $c_{\alpha\beta}$ satisfying the axioms $(A)_1$ for each $\lambda \in \Omega$. Since there could very well be several such distinct structures on the space X, it is not clear a priori that this index as defined is unique, nor how one can pass from the properties of the index on one semi-complex $X_1$ to those on another, $X_2$. To avoid the second difficulty, the following definition is made

DEFINITION (Browder [5, p.286]): Let $X_1$ and $X_2$ be two compact spaces, each equipped with the structure of a semi-complex. Let the chain mappings of the first semi-complex be denoted by $c^{(1)}_{\alpha\beta}$ and those of the second by $c^{(2)}_{\xi\zeta}$. Then a continuous mapping $h : X_1 \longrightarrow X_2$ is said to be a semi-complex mapping with respect to the given semi-complex structures on $X_1$ and $X_2$ if, given an open covering $\lambda$ of $X_2$, there exists an open covering $\lambda'$ of $X_1$ such that the following is true:

If

$$\xi > \zeta > \alpha_0(\lambda),$$
$$\alpha > \beta > \alpha_0(\lambda'),$$

$$\alpha > h^{-1}(\xi),$$
$$\beta > h^{-1}(\zeta),$$

and if the simplicial mappings $h_{\xi\alpha}$ of $N_{\alpha,1}$ into $N_{\xi,2}$ ($N_{\alpha,1}$ the nerve of x as a covering of $X_1$, $N_{\xi,2}$ the nerve of $\xi$ as a covering of $X_2$) and $h_{\zeta\beta}$ of $N_{\beta,1}$ into $N_{\zeta,2}$ are induced by the continuous mapping h, and if $c^{(1)}_{\alpha\beta}$ is a chain mapping lying in the family $C^{(1)}_{\lambda'}$ corresponding to the covering $\lambda'$ in the semi-complex structure on $X_1$, and if $c^{(2)}_{\xi\zeta}$ is a chain mapping in the family $C^{(2)}_{\lambda}$ corresponding to the covering $\lambda$ in the semi-complex structure on $X_2$, then the chain mapping

$$h_{\xi\alpha} \; c^{(1)}_{\alpha\beta} \text{ is chain homotopic to } c^{(2)}_{\xi\zeta} \; h_{\zeta\beta}$$

with a chain homotopy D, such that for every elementary chain g of $N_\beta$,

$$h(\mathrm{Sup}(g)) \cup \mathrm{Sup}(D9)$$

is contained in a single member of $\lambda$.

A category of compact spaces and continuous mappings is said to be a category of semi-complexes if each space has a specified semi-complex structure and if all the continuous mappings are semi-complex mappings.

REMARK (Browder [5, p.287]): For a member X of the family of HLC* spaces there is a largest semi-complex structure which is essentially unique, and all continuous mappings are semi-complex mappings with respect to this structure for given spaces $X_1$ and $X_2$. With this prescription, the category of HLC* spaces and all their continuous mappings is a category of semi-complexes.

Browder [5] showed that the fixed point index as defined above is unique for the category of semi-complexes, and satisfies properties (a), (b), (c) and (d) stated on p.24. In particular, the Lefschetz fixed point theorem holds for such spaces.

### 1.3. Multi-valued mappings such that the image of each point is acyclic

In 1941 Kakutani [2] extended Brouwer's fixed point theorem for the n-cell to multi-valued mappings by proving that a compact convex subset of the Euclidean space $E^n$ has the f.p.p. for upper semi-continuous closed convex set-valued mappings.

In 1946 Eilenberg and Montgomery [1] showed that a Lefschetz number can also be defined for certain multi-valued mappings of an AR into itself. In doing so, they made essential use of the Vietoris mapping theorem (Vietoris [1] ). If X and Y are compacta, then a continuous mapping $f : X \longrightarrow Y$ is said to have property (V) if, for each $y \in Y$, the set $f^{-1}(y)$ is acyclic with respect to Vietoris homology. (See Lefschetz [5, p.240] or Vietoris [1] .) The mapping theorem of Vietoris states that if $f : X \longrightarrow Y$ satisfies property (V), then the induced homomorphism $f_{*r} : H_r(X) \longrightarrow H_r(X)$ is an isomorphism onto, for all $r \geq 0$. Thus aided, the following theorems are proved:

EM1. (Eilenberg and Montgomery [1] ). Let X be an ANR and Y a compactum. Let $g,h : Y \longrightarrow X$ be continuous functions, of which g satisfies property (V). Let $\Lambda(g,h) = \sum(-1)^r \text{ trace } (h_{*r}g_{*r}^{-1})$. If $\Lambda(g,h) \neq 0$, then there exists a point $y_0 \in Y$ such that $g(y_0) = h(y_0)$.

EM2. (Eilenberg and Montgomery [1] ). Let X be an ANR and $f : X \longrightarrow \mathcal{C}(X)$ upper semi-continuous, where $\mathcal{C}(X)$ denotes the family of non-empty closed acyclic subsets of X. Let $Y = \{(x,x') \in X \times X \mid x' \in f(x)\}$. Define the mappings $g,h : Y \longrightarrow X$ as follows: $g(x,x') = x$, $h(x,x') = x'$. Then g satisfies property (V) ($g^{-1}(x)$ is homeomorphic to $f(x)$), and we can form the Lefschetz number $\Lambda(f) = \Lambda(g,h) = \sum(-1)^r \text{ trace } (h_{*r}g_{*r}^{-1})$. Then, if $\Lambda(f) \neq 0$, there exists a point $x_0 \in X$ such that $x_0 \in f(x_0)$.

This implies the following generalization of Kakutani's theorem:

EM3. (Eilenberg and Montgomery [1] ). Let X be an acyclic ANR and $f : X \longrightarrow \mathcal{C}(X)$ upper semi-continuous, where $\mathcal{C}(X)$ denotes the family of non-empty closed acyclic subsets of X. Then there exists a point $x_o \in X$ such that $x_o \in f(x_o)$.

Using convexity arguments, Bohnenblust and Karlin [1] (1950), extended Kakutani's theorem to Banach spaces, and it was then extended to locally convex topological linear spaces simultaneously by Fan [1] and Glicksberg [1] in 1952.

Let X be a Banach space and $\mathcal{C}(X)$ the family of non-empty closed convex subsets of X. Browder [3] (1959) called a mapping $f : X \to \mathcal{C}(X)$ completely continuous if the following conditions hold:

(i) The graph of f, $G(f) = \{(x,y) \mid x,y \in X,\ y \in f(x)\}$, is a closed subset of $X \times X$.

(ii) For every bounded subset S of X, there exists a compact subset $K_S$ of X such that $f(x) \cap K_S \neq \emptyset$ for $x \in S$.

(iii) Let K and $K_1$ be compact subsets of X such that $f(x) \cap K_1 \neq \emptyset$ for $x \in K$. Let $x_o$ be a point of K and $\varepsilon$ a positive constant. Then there exists $\delta > 0$ such that, for $x \in K$ with $\|x-x_o\| < \delta$, we have $f(x) \cap K_1 \subset U_\varepsilon(f(x)) \cap K_1$ and $f(x_o) \cap K_1 \subset U_\varepsilon(f(x)) \cap K_1$.

Browder [3] showed that if $f : X \to \mathcal{C}(X)$ is a completely continuous mapping such that, for some positive integer m, $f^m[X]$ is a bounded set, then X has a fixed point under f.

In 1952, Begle [2] proved a very general form of the fixed point formula which includes the results of Eilenberg and Montgomery [1], and those of Fan [1] and Glicksberg [1]. The proof uses only homology theory and none of the homotopy properties involved in the notion of an ANR. Consequently, the theorem is shown to hold for a much larger class of spaces, which he calls lc spaces. The lc spaces of Begle [3] are the same as the HLC* spaces of Lefschetz [5]. (Also see Lefschetz [6,p.123-126] and Begle [1].) The proof also makes essential use of the Vietoris mapping theorem, for which he gives an extension to compact spaces, using a generalized form of Vietoris cycles.

We now proceed to state and prove Begle's theorems as in Begle [2,3].

DEFINITIONS (Begle [2]):

Only compact Hausdorff spaces are considered. By a covering $\mu$ of a space X we shall always mean a finite covering consisting of open sets. In this section we shall write $\nu<\mu$ if $\nu$ is a refinement of $\mu$. If A is a subset of X, we denote by St $(A,\mu)$ the set $\cup\{U \in \mu \mid A \cap U \neq \emptyset\}$, and by St $(\mu,\mu)$ or $\mu^*$ we denote the covering $\{St\ (U,\mu) \mid U \in \mu\}$. If $\mu^* < \nu$, we say that $\mu$ is a star refinement of $\nu$, and we write $\mu <^* \nu$. Every covering has a star refinement (Tuckey [1,p.47]). For each covering $\mu$, we choose one of its star refinements and denote it by $^*\mu$.

An n-simplex $\sigma_n$ of X is a set of n+1 points of X, and these are the vertices of $\sigma_n$. If $\mu$ is a covering and A a subset of X, we write diam $A < \mu$ if there exists $U \in \mu$ such that $A \subset U$. $X(\mu)$ is the simplicial complex consisting of all simplexes $\sigma$ such that diam $\sigma < \mu$. Clearly, if $\nu < \mu$, then $X(\nu)$ is a subcomplex of $X(\mu)$. If A is a subset of X, then $X(\mu) \cap A$ is the subcomplex of $X(\mu)$ consisting of all the simplexes of $X(\mu)$ which are contained in A.

We shall consider only finite chains on the complexes $X(\mu)$. The coefficients, unless otherwise stated, are in an arbitrary Abelian group. If $c_n$ is such a chain, we denote by $|c_n|$ the finite simplicial complex consisting of all the simplexes on which $c_n$ has non-zero coefficients together with all their faces.

In what follows we make frequent use of the Cartesian product of a simplicial complex K and the closed unit interval $I = [0,1]$, so we recall here the definition of this product (Lefschetz [5,p.307]). Let the vertices of K be simply ordered in an arbitrary fashion. Let $\{a_i'\}_{i=1}^{m}$ be a copy of the collection $\{a_i\}_{i=1}^{m}$ of vertices of K. For each n-simplex $\sigma_n=(a_0,a_1,\ldots,a_n)$ of K, consider the n+1 simplexes of the form $(a_0,a_1,\ldots,a_i,a_i',\ldots,a_n')$. The collection of all such simplexes, together with all their faces, constitute the product $K \times I$. K is called the base of $K \times I$, and the set of all simplexes of $K \times I$, all of whose vertices are primed, is called the top of $K \times I$.

For each simplex $\sigma_n = (a_0,a_1,\ldots,a_n)$ of K, let $D(\sigma_n) = \sum_{i=0}^{n} (-1)^i (a_0,a_1,\ldots,a_i,a_i',\ldots,a_n')$, and if $c_n = \Sigma g_j \sigma_n^j$, let $D(c_n) = \Sigma g_j D(\sigma_n^j)$. For any chain $c_n$ of K, a direct calculation shows that

$$FD(c_n) + DF(c_n) = c'_n - c_n,$$

where $c'_n$ is the chain in the top of $K \times I$ formed by replacing each vertex of each simplex of $c_n$ by the corresponding primed vertex, and F is the boundary operator. Hence, if $z_n$ is a cycle of K,

$$FD(z_n) = z'_n - z_n,$$

i.e. $z_n \sim z'_n$ on $K \times I$.

In one place (lemma 3) it will be convenient to consider $K \times I$ as a cell complex rather than as a simplicial complex. This time the elements of $K \times I$ are all the cells of the form $\sigma \times 0$, $\sigma \times 1$ or $\sigma \times I$, where $\sigma$ runs through the simplexes of K. The boundary relations in $K \times I$ are:
$F(\sigma \times 0) = (F\sigma) \times 0$, $F(\sigma \times 1) = (F\sigma) \times 1$, and $F(\sigma \times I) = (F\sigma) \times I + (\sigma \times 1) - (\sigma \times 0)$. Then for any cycle z on K, we have $F(z \times I) = (z \times 1) - (z \times 0)$, i.e. $z \times 1 \sim z \times 0$ on $K \times I$.

A collection $z_n = \{z_n(\mu)\}$ of n-cycles of X, one for each covering $\mu$ of X, is a generalized <u>Vietoris n-cycle</u> <u>(n-V-cycle)</u> if $z_n(\mu)$ is a cycle of $X(\mu)$ and if, whenever $\nu < \mu$, $z_n(\nu) \sim z_n(\mu)$ on $X(\mu)$. The cycles $z_n(\mu)$ are the <u>coordinates</u> of $z_n$. If $z_n$ and $z'_n$ are two n-V-cycles, then $z_n + z'_n$ is the n-V-cycle whose coordinate on $X(\mu)$ is $z_n(\mu) + z'_n(\mu)$. Further, $z_n \sim 0$ if $z_n(\mu) \sim 0$ on $X(\mu)$ for every $\mu$. The <u>n-dimensional Vietoris homology group</u> of X, $H^V_n(X)$, is the factor group of the group of n-V-cycles of X by the subgroup of those which bound.

Let X and Y be two spaces and $f : X \longrightarrow Y$ a continuous mapping. Let $z_n$ be an n-V-cycle of X. For each covering $\nu$ of Y, $\mu = f^{-1}(\nu)$ is a covering of X. Clearly, f maps each simplex of $X(\mu)$ onto a simplex of $Y(\nu)$, and hence is a simplicial mapping of $X(\mu)$ into $Y(\nu)$. We define $f(z_n)$ to be the n-V-cycle of Y whose coordinate on $Y(\nu)$ is $f(z_n(\mu))$. This clearly induces a homomorphism of $H^V_n(X)$ into $H^V_n(Y)$.

The Vietoris homology groups defined above do not give any new homology properties of X. If X is compact metric, it is easy to see that $H^V_n(X)$ is isomorphic to the ordinary Vietoris homology group. In the general case, these groups are isomorphic to the corresponding Čech groups, as we now show.

Given a covering $\mu$ of X, let $\nu = {}^*\mu$. For each vertex a of $X(\nu)$, choose an element $V \in \nu$ such that $a \in V$ and then choose an element $U \in \mu$ such that $St(V,\nu) \subset U$. Set $\Theta(a) = U$. Then $\Theta$ is a simplicial mapping of $X(\nu)$ into the nerve $N(\mu)$ of $\mu$.

Next, given a covering $\nu$, let $\xi = {}^*\nu$. For each element $W \in \xi$, let $\varphi(W)$ be a point in W. Then $\varphi$ is a simplicial mapping of $N(\xi)$ into $X(\nu)$.

Now, let $y_n$ be an n-V-cycle. For each covering $\mu$, let $\nu = {}^*\mu$ and define $z_n(\mu)$ to be $\Theta\, y_n(\nu)$. We assert that $z_n = \{z_n(\mu)\}$ is a Čech cycle and that $\Theta$ induces an isomorphism of $H_n^V(X)$ onto $H_n^c(X)$, the n-dimensional Čech homology group of X.

To see that $z_n$ is a Čech cycle, let $\mu_2 < \mu_1$ be two coverings of X. Let $\nu_1 = {}^*\mu_1$ and $\nu_2 = {}^*\mu_2$, and choose a common refinement $\nu$ of $\nu_1$ and $\nu_2$. By the definition of $z_n$, we have

$$z_n(\mu_1) = \Theta_1\, y_n(\nu_1),$$

$$z_n(\mu_2) = \Theta_2\, y_n(\nu_2).$$

Since $\nu < \nu_1$,

$$y_n(\nu) \sim y_n(\nu_1) \text{ on } X(\nu_1).$$

Therefore

$$\Theta_1 y_n(\nu) \sim \Theta_1 y_n(\nu_1) \text{ on } N(\mu_1).$$

Similarly, since $\nu < \nu_2$,

$$\Theta_2 y_n(\nu) \sim \Theta_2 y_n(\nu_2) \text{ on } N(\mu_2),$$

and hence

$$\pi\Theta_2 y_n(\nu) \sim \pi\Theta_2 y_n(\nu_2) \text{ on } N(\mu_1),$$

where $\pi$ is the projection of $N(\mu_2)$ into $N(\mu_1)$. Thus it will be sufficient to show that

(1) $$\pi\,\Theta_2 y_n(\nu) \sim \Theta_1 y_n(\nu) \quad \text{on } N(\mu_1).$$

In order to show this, let $K = |y_n(\nu)|$. We define a simplicial mapping $\psi$ of $K \times I$ into $N(\mu_1)$. For each vertex a of the base of $K \times I$, let $\psi(a) = \pi\Theta_2(a)$, and for each vertex a' of the top of $K \times I$, let $\psi(a') = \Theta_1(a)$.

To see that this is indeed a simplicial mapping, let

$(a_0, a_1, \ldots, a_i, a_i', \ldots, a_n')$ be a simplex of $K \times I$. By the definition of $\Theta_2$, there is, for $0 \leq j \leq i$, a set $V_{2j} \in \nu_2$ containing $a_j$, and a set $U_{2j} = \Theta_2(a_j) \in \mu_2$ containing St $(V_{2j}, \nu_2)$. By the definition of $\Pi$, there is a set $U_{1j} = \Pi\Theta_2(a_j) \in \mu_1$ containing $U_{2j}$. Similarly, for $i \leq k \leq n$, there is a set $V_{1k}' \in \nu_1$ containing $a_k$ and a set $U_{1k}' = \psi(a_k')$ containing St $(V_{1k}', \nu_1)$.

Since $(a_0, \ldots, a_n)$ is a simplex of $X(\nu)$, there is a set $V \in \nu$ containing $a_0, \ldots, a_n$. Therefore, since $\nu < \nu_2$, $V \subset$ St $(V_{2j}, \nu_2)$ for $0 \leq j \leq i$, and consequently $V \subset U_{1j}$ for $0 \leq j \leq i$. Similarly, since $\nu < \nu_1$, $V \subset$ St $(V_{1k}', \nu_1)$ and hence $V \subset U_{1k}'$ for $i \leq k \leq n$. Therefore $U_{10} \cap U_{11} \cap \ldots \cap U_{1i} \cap U_{1i}' \cap \ldots U_{1n}' \neq \emptyset$. Thus $\psi$ maps the vertices of $(a_0, \ldots, a_i, a_i', \ldots, a_n')$ into the vertices of a simplex of $N(\mu_1)$ and therefore is simplicial.

Now $y_n(\nu) \sim y_n'(\nu)$ on $K \times I$. By the definition of $\psi$, $\psi(y_n(\nu)) = \Pi\Theta_2(y_n(\nu))$ and $\psi(y_n'(\nu)) = \Theta_1(y_n(\nu))$, and this proves (1).

If $y_n \sim 0$, then clearly $z_n \sim 0$ also. Suppose now that $z_n \sim 0$. We shall show that $y_n \sim 0$. Given any covering $\mu$, let $\nu = {}^*\mu$ and let $\xi = {}^*\nu$. Since $y_n(\xi) \sim y_n(\mu)$ on $X(\mu)$, it will be sufficient to show that $y_n(\xi) \sim 0$ on $X(\mu)$. Now $z_n(\nu) = y_n(\xi) \sim 0$ on $N(\nu)$. Hence $\varphi\Theta y_n(\xi) \sim 0$ on $X(\mu)$, so we are reduced to proving

(2) $$y_n(\xi) \sim \varphi\Theta y_n(\xi) \text{ on } X(\mu).$$

Let $K = |y_n(\xi)|$. We define a simplicial mapping $\omega$ of $K \times I$ into $X(\mu)$ in the following way: For each vertex a in the base of $K \times I$, let $\omega(a) = a$, and for each vertex $a'$ in the top of $K \times I$, let $\omega(a') = \varphi\Theta(a)$.

To see that $\omega$ is simplicial, let $(a_0, a_1, \ldots, a_i, a_i', \ldots, a_n')$ be a simplex of $K \times I$. By the definition of $\Theta$, there is a set $W_k' \in \xi$ containing $a_k$ and a set $V_k' \in \nu$ containing St $(W_k', \xi)$. By the definition of $\varphi$, $\varphi(V_k') \in V_k'$.

Since $(a_0, a_1, \ldots, a_n)$ is a simplex of $X(\xi)$, there is a set $W \in \xi$ containing $(a_0, a_1, \ldots, a_n)$. Hence $W \subset$ St $(W_k', \xi)$ for $i \leq k \leq n$ and therefore $W \subset V_k'$. Thus $V_n' \cap V_k' \neq \emptyset$, $i \leq k \leq n$, so $V_k' \subset$ St $(V_n', \nu)$. Since $\nu = {}^*\mu$, there is an element $U \in \mu$ which contains St $(V_n', \nu)$, and hence each $V_k'$. Consequently $\varphi\Theta(a_k) \subset U$, $i \leq k \leq n$. But $W \subset V_n' \subset U$, so $(a_0, a_1, \ldots, a_n) \subset U$. Hence all the vertices of $(a_0, a_1, \ldots, a_i, a_i', \ldots, a_n')$ are carried by $\omega$ into vertices contained in one element of $\mu$ and hence into the vertices of a simplex of $X(\mu)$, and therefore $\omega$ is a simplicial mapping.

Now $y_n(\xi) \sim y'_n(\xi)$ on $K \times I$. By the definition of $\omega$, $\omega(y_n(\xi)) = y_n(\xi)$ and $\omega(y'_n(\xi)) = \varphi\Theta(y_n(\xi))$, so we have proved (2).

Thus far we have shown that $\Theta$ induces an isomorphism of $H_n^V(X)$ into $H_n^C(X)$. To complete the proof we must show that this isomorphism is onto, i.e. that for every Čech cycle $z_n$ there is an n-V-cycle $y_n$ such that $\Theta y_n \sim z_n$. But, given $z_n$ and a covering $\mu$, let $\nu = {}^*\mu$. Define $y_n(\mu)$ to be $\varphi(z_n(\nu))$. Then $y_n = \{y_n(\mu)\}$ is an n-V-cycle and $\Theta y_n \sim z_n$. We omit the proofs of these last two statements since they are analogous to those above.

Let X and Y be compact spaces. A continuous mapping $f : X \longrightarrow Y$ is a Vietoris mapping of order n if for each covering $\mu$ of X and each point $y \in Y$ there is a covering $\xi = \xi(\mu, y)$ of X, with $\xi < \mu$, such that any k-cycle, $0 \le k \le n$, on $X(\xi) \cap f^{-1}(y)$ bounds on $X(\mu) \cap f^{-1}(y)$.

We can now formulate the Vietoris mapping theorem needed in the proof of the fixed point theorem.

THEOREM 1 (Begle [2] ). If $f : X \rightarrow Y$ is a Vietoris mapping of order n of X onto Y, then the homomorphism of $H_n^V(X)$ into $H_n^V(Y)$ induced by f is an isomorphism and is onto.

The hypothesis of the theorem can be put in a more convenient form if the coefficient group is restricted to lie in either of two classes of groups, the class of fields and the class of elementary compact topological groups (Steenrod [1, p.672]). The latter class consists of the character groups of discrete groups with finite bases, and hence contains all finite groups as well as the group of real numbers mod 1.

THEOREM 2 (Begle [2] ). If the coefficient group is an elementary compact topological group or is a field, and f is a mapping of X onto Y such that for each point $y \in Y$, and for each integer k, $0 \le k \le n$, the augmented Vietoris homology group $H_k^V(f^{-1}(y))$ is trivial, then the homomorphism of $H_n(X)$ into $H_n(Y)$ induced by f is an isomorphism and is onto.

A number of lemmas will be needed.

LEMMA 1 (Begle [2]). If f is a Vietoris mapping of order n of X onto Y, then for each covering $\mu$ of X and each covering $\nu$ of Y there is a refinement $\gamma = \gamma(\mu,\nu)$ of $\nu$ such that if B is a subset of Y with diam $B < \gamma$, then there is a point $y \in Y$ such that

1) $St(y,\nu) \supset B$;
2) $St(f^{-1}(y), {}^*\xi) \supset f^{-1}(B)$,

where $\xi = \xi(\mu, y)$.

PROOF: For each $y \in Y$, let $A_y = X \setminus St(f^{-1}(y), {}^*\xi)$. Then $A_y$ is closed, hence compact, so $f[A_y]$ is closed and $y \notin f[A_y]$. Since Y is normal, there is an open set $B_y$ such that $y \in B_y$ and $B_y \cap f[A_y] = \emptyset$. We may choose $B_y$ to be in a set of $\nu$ which contains y. Now a finite number of the sets $B_y$ cover Y, and these constitute the covering $\gamma$.

LEMMA 2 (Begle [2]). If f is a Vietoris mapping of order n of X onto Y, then for each covering $\mu$ of X and each covering $\nu$ of Y there is a covering $\eta = \eta(\mu,\nu)$ of Y, with $\eta < \nu$, and a chain mapping t of the (n+1)-skeleton of $Y(\eta)$ into $X(\mu)$ such that for any k-simplex $\sigma_k$ of $Y(\eta)$, $0 \le k \le n+1$, $ft\,\sigma_k$ is a barycentric subdivision $b\,\sigma_k$ of $\sigma_k$ with diam $|b\,\sigma_k| < \nu$.

PROOF: Let $\mu_{n+1} = \mu$ and $\nu_{n+1} = \nu$. Let $\gamma_n = \gamma(\mu_{n+1}, {}^*\nu_{n+1})$ and let $\nu_n = {}^*\gamma_n$. For each element $Q_{ni}$ of $\gamma_n$, diam $Q_{ni} < \gamma_n$, so by lemma 1, there is an associated point $y_{ni}$. Let $\xi_{ni} = \xi(\mu_{n+1}, y_{ni})$ and let $\mu_n$ be a common refinement of the coverings $\xi_{ni}$. Next, let $\gamma_{n-1} = \gamma(\mu_n, {}^*\nu_n)$ and let $\nu_{n-1} = {}^*\gamma_{n-1}$. Let $\{y_{n-1,i}\}$ be the points associated, by lemma 1, with the elements of $\gamma_{n-1}$, and let $\xi_{n-1,i} = \xi(\mu_n, y_{n-1,i})$. Let $\mu_{n-1}$ be a common refinement of the coverings ${}^*\xi_{n-1,i}$.

Proceeding in this fashion, we construct a sequence $\{\mu_k\}$ of coverings of X and a sequence $\{\nu_k\}$ of coverings of Y, together with the associated sets $\{y_{ki}\}$, such that

1) $\nu_{k-1} = {}^*\gamma_{k-1}$; $\gamma_{k-1} = \gamma(\mu_k, {}^*\nu_k)$;

2) $\mu_{k-1} < {}^*\xi(\mu_k, y_{k-1,i})$.

We assert that the covering $\nu_0$ will serve for $\eta(\mu,\nu)$. To prove this, we must construct the chain mapping t. First, let $\sigma_0$

be a vertex of $Y(\nu_0)$. Let $s_0$ be an arbitrary point of $f^{-1}(\sigma_0)$, and define $t(\sigma_0)$ to be $s_0$. Then $t(\sigma_0)$ is a null-chain of $X(\mu_0)$, and $ft\,\sigma_0 = \sigma_0$.

Now suppose that t has been defined for all simplexes $\sigma_m$ in $Y(\nu_0)$ with $m < k$ in such a way that $t(\sigma_m)$ is a chain of $X(\mu_m)$ and $ft\,\sigma_m$ is a barycentric subdivision $b\sigma_m$ of $\sigma_m$, with diam $|b\sigma_m| < \nu_m$.

Let $\sigma_k$ be a k-simplex of $Y(\nu_0)$. Then t is defined on $F\sigma_k$, and $tF\sigma_k$ is a chain of $X(\mu_{k-1})$. Now consider $f|tF\sigma_k|$. Since $\sigma_k$ is in $Y(\nu_0)$, there is an element $V_0$ of $\nu_0$ which contains $\sigma_k$. If $\sigma_{k-1}$ appears in $F\sigma_k$, then $ft\sigma_{k-1} = \sigma_{k-1}$ contains a vertex of $\sigma_k$. But diam $|b\sigma_{k-1}| < \nu_{k-1}$, so $St(V_0, \nu_{k-1})$ contains $f|tF\sigma_k|$. But $\nu_0 < \nu_{k-1} < \gamma_{k-1}$, so diam $f|tF\sigma_k| < \gamma_{k-1} = \gamma(\mu_k, {}^*\nu_k)$. Let $y_{k-1,1}$ be the corresponding point of Y, so that $St(y_{k-1,1}, {}^*\nu_k)$ contains $f|tF\sigma_k|$ and $St(f^{-1}(y_{k-1,1}), {}^*\xi)$ contains $f^{-1}f|tF\sigma_k|$, which in turn contains $|tF\sigma_k|$, where $\xi = \xi(\mu_k, y_{k-1,1})$.

Denote now the cycle $tF\sigma_k$ by $z_{k-1}$, and let $K = |z_{k-1}|$. We define a simplicial mapping $\chi$ of $K \times I$ into $X(\xi)$ by first setting $\chi(a) = a$ for each vertex a in the base of $K \times I$. Next, let a' be a vertex in the top of $K \times I$, and let a be the corresponding point in the base, so that a is a vertex of $|tF\sigma_k|$. Since $St(f^{-1}(y_{k-1,1}), {}^*\xi)$ contains $|tF\sigma_k|$, there is a set ${}^*W$ of ${}^*\xi$ which meets $f^{-1}(y_{k-1,1})$ and also contains a. Let $\chi(a')$ be a point in ${}^*W \cap f^{-1}(y_{k-1,1})$. If now $(a_0, \ldots, a_i, a_i', \ldots, a_{k-1}')$ is a simplex of $K \times I$, then $(a_0, \ldots, a_{k-1})$ is a simplex of $|tF\sigma_k|$ and hence is contained in some element $U_{k-1}$ of $\mu_{k-1}$. For each j, $i \leq j \leq k-1$, $\chi(a_j')$ is a point of ${}^*W_j$, where $a_j \in {}^*W_j$, and therefore $\chi(a_0, \ldots, a_i, a_i', \ldots, a_{k-1}') =$
$= (a_0, \ldots, a_i, \chi(a_i'), \ldots, \chi(a_{k-1}'))$ is in $St(U_{k-1}, {}^*\xi)$, and hence in some element of $\xi$, since $\mu_{k-1} < {}^*\xi$. Thus $\chi$ maps $K \times I$ simplicially into $X(\xi)$.

Now let $s_k^1 = \chi(Dz_{k-1})$, so that $Fs_k^1 = \chi(z_{k-1}') - \chi(z_{k-1}) = \chi(z_{k-1}') - z_{k-1}$. The cycle $\chi(z_{k-1}')$ is on $X(\xi) \cap f^{-1}(y_{k-1,1})$, and since $\xi = \xi(\mu_k, y_{k-1,1})$, there is a chain $s_k^2$ on $X(\mu_k) \cap f^{-1}(y_{k-1,1})$ such that $Fs_k^2 = \chi(z_{k-1}')$. Let $s_k = s_k^2 - s_k^1$, and set $t\sigma_k = s_k$. Then $Ft\sigma_k = tF\sigma_k$, so t is a chain mapping.

Finally, observe that each vertex of $|s_k|$ is either a vertex of $|tF\sigma_k|$ or is a vertex in $f^{-1}(y_{k-1,1})$ and f maps all the latter on the single point $y_{k-1,1}$. Hence $fs_k$ is the join of $y_{k-1,1}$ with

$ftF\sigma_k = bF\sigma_k$ and thus is a barycentric subdivision $b\sigma_k$ of $\sigma_k$. Since $St(y_{k-1,1}, {}^*\nu_k)$ contains $f|tF\sigma_k|$, diam $|b\sigma_k| < \nu_k$.

Thus we can continue extending the definition of t until it is finally defined on all of the (n+1)-skeleton of $Y(\nu_0)$, and we have therefore completed the proof of the lemma.

LEMMA 3 (Begle [2]). Let $\mu$ and $\bar{\mu}$ be coverings of X, with $\bar{\mu} < \mu$, and let $\nu$ and $\bar{\nu}$ be coverings of Y. Let $\eta = \eta(\mu,\nu)$ and $\bar{\eta} = \eta(\bar{\mu},\bar{\nu})$. Let t and $\bar{t}$ be the corresponding chain mappings. Then there is a common refinement $\lambda$ of $\eta$ and $\bar{\eta}$ such that for any cycle $z_n$ on $Y(\lambda)$, $tz_n \sim \bar{t}z_n$ on $X(\mu)$.

PROOF: We first recall the sequences $\{\mu_k\}$ and $\{\nu_k\}$ of coverings which were constructed in the proof of lemma 2. Suppose now that we construct new sequences $\{\mu'_k\}$ and $\{\nu^1_k\}$ by first choosing $\mu'_{n+1}$ to be any refinement of $\mu$ and $\nu'_{n+1}$ to be any refinement of $\nu$. Then, at each step, choose $\gamma'_k$ to be a common refinement of $\gamma_k$ and of $\gamma(\mu'_{k+1}, {}^*\nu'_{k+1})$, and $\nu'_k$ to be a common refinement of ${}^*\gamma'_k$ and of $\nu_k$. Let $\{y'_{ki}\}$ be the set of points of Y associated with $\gamma'_k$, and let $\mu'_k$ be a common refinement of $\mu_k$ and of the coverings $\xi'_{ki}$, where $\xi'_{ki} = \xi(\mu'_{k+1}, y'_{ki})$.

Now we can repeat the argument of lemma 2 to obtain a chain mapping t' of $Y(\nu'_0)$ into $X(\mu'_{n+1})$ such that for $\sigma_k$ in $Y(\nu'_0)$, $t'\sigma_k$ is a chain of $X(\mu'_k)$. We assert that for any cycle $z_n$ on $Y(\nu'_0)$, $tz_n \sim t'z_n$ on $X(\mu)$.

Before proving this assertion, we show that the lemma follows from it. For we can choose $\mu'_k$ and $\bar{\mu}'_k$ to be the same covering of X for each k, and similarly for $\nu'_k$ and $\bar{\nu}'_k$. Then $\nu'_0 = \bar{\nu}'_0$, and we take this to be $\lambda$. Now, if $z_n$ is a cycle on $Y(\lambda)$, $tz_n \sim t'z_n$ on $X(\mu)$ by our assertion, and similarly, $\bar{t}z_n \sim t'z_n$ on $X(\bar{\mu})$. But t' and $\bar{t}'$ are the same chain mapping, and $X(\bar{\mu})$ is a subcomplex of $X(\mu)$, so $tz_n \sim \bar{t}z_n$ on $X(\mu)$.

Returning now to the assertion above, let $z_n$ be a cycle of $Y(\nu'_0)$ and let $K = |z_n|$. We shall define a chain mapping u of the cell complex $K \times I$ into $X(\mu)$. For a cell of $K \times I$ of the form $\sigma \times 0$, let $u(\sigma \times 0) = t'(\sigma)$, and for a cell of the form $\sigma \times 1$, let $u(\sigma \times 1) = t(\sigma)$. Now consider a vertex $\sigma_0$ of K. $t(\sigma_0) = s_0$ and $t'(\sigma_0) = s'_0$ are, by construction, vertices $f^{-1}(\sigma_0)$ and $ft(\sigma_0) = ft'(\sigma_0) = \sigma_0$. There is a point, $y_{02}$, such that $St(y_{02}, \nu_0)$ contains $\sigma_0$ and $St(f^{-1}(y_{02}, {}^*\xi)$ contains $f^{-1}(\sigma_0)$, where $\xi = \xi(\mu_1, y_{02})$. Let

$c_0 = t\sigma_0 - t'\sigma_0$, a cycle, and let $L_0 = |c_0|$. We map the simplicial complex $L_0 \times I$ into $X(\xi)$ by a mapping $\omega_0$ such that $\omega_0(a) = a$ for any vertex $a$ in the base of $L_0 \times I$, and $\omega_0(a')$ is a point of $f^{-1}(y_{02})$ such that $St(\omega_0(a'), {}^*\xi)$ contains $a$. That there exists such a point follows from the fact that $St(f^{-1}(y_{02}), {}^*\xi)$ contains $L_0$. It is clear that $\omega_0$ is a simplicial mapping of $L_0 \times I$ into $X(\xi)$. Let $c_1^1 = \omega_0(Dc_0)$, so that $c_1^1$ is a chain of $X(\xi)$ and $F(c_1^1) = \omega_0(c_o') - c_0$. Now $\omega_0(c_o')$ is a cycle of $X(\xi) \cap f^{-1}(y_{02})$, so there is a one-chain $c_1^2$ of $X(\mu_1) \cap f^{-1}(y_{02})$ such that $Fc_1^2 = \omega_0(c_o')$. Then $c_1 = c_1^2 - c_1^1$ is a chain of $X(\mu_1)$ and $Fc_1 = c_0$. Clearly $f|c_1|$ is the join of $\sigma_0$ and $y_{02}$. We define $u(\sigma_0 \times I)$ to be $c_1$. Then $Fu(\sigma_0 \times I) = c_0 = t\sigma_0 - t'\sigma_0 = u(\sigma_0 \times 1) - u(\sigma_0 \times 0) = F(\sigma_0 \times I)$.

Now suppose that $u$ has been defined on every cell of $K \times I$ of the form $\sigma_m \times I$, for all $m < k$, in such a way that $u(\sigma_m \times I)$ is a chain of $X(\mu_{m+1})$ and $\operatorname{diam} f|u(\sigma_m \times I)| < \nu_{m+1}$. Let $\sigma_k$ be a simplex of $Y(\nu_0')$. Then $u$ is defined on $F(\sigma_k \times I)$, and we wish to consider the set $f|uF(\sigma_k \times I)|$. But $F(\sigma_k \times I) = (F(\sigma_k) \times I) + (\sigma_k \times 1) - (\sigma_k \times 0)$, so $f|uF(\sigma_k \times I)|$ is contained in

$$f|u(F(\sigma_k) \times I)| \cup f|t\sigma_k| \cup f|t'\sigma_k| .$$

Let $V_0'$ be an element of $\nu_0'$ which contains $\sigma_k$. Since $\operatorname{diam} f|t\sigma_k| < \nu_k$, $St(V_0', \nu_k)$ contains $f|t\sigma_k|$. Similarly, since $\nu_k' < \nu_k$, $St(V_0', \nu_k)$ contains $f|t'\sigma_k|$. Also, for any simplex $\sigma_{k-1}$ in $F\sigma_k$, $\operatorname{diam} f|u(\sigma_{k-1} \times I)| < \nu_k$ and $f|u(\sigma_{k-1} \times I)|$ contains a vertex of $\sigma_k$, so $St(V_0', \nu_k)$ also contains $f|u(F(\sigma_k) \times I)|$. But $\nu_k < {}^*\gamma_k$, where $\gamma_k = \gamma(\mu_{k+1}, {}^*\nu_{k+1})$, so $\operatorname{diam} f|u\,F(\sigma_k \times I)| < \gamma_k$.

Therefore there is a point, say $y_{k2}$, such that $St(y_{k2}, {}^*\nu_{k+1})$ contains $f|uF(\sigma_k \times I)|$ and $St(f^{-1}(y_{k2}), {}^*\xi)$ contains $f^{-1}f|uF(\sigma_k \times I)| \supset |uF(\sigma_k \times I)|$, where $\xi = \xi(\mu_{k+1}, y_{k2})$.

Now let $c_k = uF(\sigma_k \times I)$, and let $L_k = |c_k|$. We can define a simplicial mapping $\omega_k$ of the simplicial complex $L_k \times I$ into $X(\xi)$ in the same way that we defined $\omega_0$, so that $F\omega_k(Dc_k) = \omega_k(c_k') - c_k$, and $\omega_k(c_k')$ is a cycle of $X(\xi) \cap f^{-1}(y_{k2})$. Let $c_{k+1}^1 = \omega_k(Dc_k)$ and let $c_{k+1}^2$ be a chain of $X(\mu_{k+1}) \cap f^{-1}(y_{k2})$ such that $F(c_{k+1}^2) = \omega_k(c_k')$. Then set $u(\sigma_k \times I) = c_{k+1} = c_{k+1}^2 - c_{k+1}^1$. We have $Fu(\sigma_k \times I) = Fc_{k+1} = c_k = uF(\sigma_k \times I)$, so $u$ commutes with $F$. Also, $f|u(\sigma_k \times I)|$ is the join of $f|uF(\sigma_k \times I)|$ and $y_{k2}$. Since $St(y_{k2}, {}^*\nu_{k+1})$ contains $f|uF(\sigma_k \times I)|$, $\operatorname{diam} f|u(\sigma_k \times I)| < \nu_{k+1}$. By construction, $u(\sigma_k \times I)$ is on $X(\mu_{k+1})$.

We can therefore continue extending the definition of u until it is defined on all the cells of $K \times I$. Now $F(z_n \times I) = (z_n \times 1) - (z_n \times 0)$ in $K \times I$, so $uF(z_n \times I) = Fu(z_n \times I) = u(z_n \times 1) - u(z_n \times 0) = tz_n - t'z_n$. Since $u(z_n \times I)$ is a chain of $X(\mu_{n+1}) = X(\mu)$, $tz_n \sim t'z_n$ on $X(\mu)$, which completes the proof of the lemma.

PROOF OF THEOREM 1: We show first that under the homomorphism induced by f, each element of $H_n^V(Y)$ is the image of an element of $H_n^V(X)$.

For each covering $\mu$ of X we choose a covering $\nu$ of Y such that $\mu$ is a refinement of $f^{-1}(\nu)$ and if $\mu = f^{-1}(\nu)$ for some $\nu$, we choose this $\nu$. Let $z_n = \{z(\nu)\}$ be an n-V-cycle of Y. For each covering $\mu$ of X, we define $y_n(\mu)$ to be $tz_n(\eta)$, where $\eta = \eta(\mu, \nu)$, $\nu$ being the covering associated with $\mu$ as above, and t being the chain mapping of $Y(\eta)$ into $X(\mu)$ given by lemma 2.

We assert that the collection $\{y_n(\mu)\}$ is an n-V-cycle. For, let $\bar{\mu}$ be a refinement of $\mu$, and let $\bar{\nu}$ be the covering of Y associated with $\bar{\mu}$. Then $y_n(\mu) = tz_n(\eta)$ and $y_n(\bar{\mu}) = \bar{t}z_n(\bar{\eta})$, where $\bar{\eta} = \eta(\bar{\mu}, \bar{\nu})$. Let $\lambda$ be the common refinement of $\eta$ and $\bar{\eta}$ given by lemma 3. Then $tz_n(\lambda) \sim \bar{t}z_n(\lambda)$ on $X(\mu)$. Since $z_n$ is an n-V-cycle, $z_n(\lambda) \sim z_n(\eta)$ on $Y(\eta)$. Hence $tz_n(\lambda) \sim tz_n(\eta)$ on $X(\mu)$. Similarly, $\bar{t}z_n(\lambda) \sim \bar{t}z_n(\bar{\eta})$ on $X(\bar{\mu})$. But $X(\bar{\mu})$ is a subcomplex of $X(\mu)$, so $y_n(\bar{\mu}) = \bar{t}z_n(\bar{\eta}) \sim tz_n(\eta) = y_n(\mu)$ on $X(\mu)$, which proves that $\{y_n(\mu)\}$ is an n-V-cycle.

Next, $fy_n \sim z_n$. For a given covering $\nu$ of Y, let $\mu = f^{-1}(\nu)$. Then $y_n(\mu) = tz_n(\eta)$, where $\eta = \eta(\mu, \nu)$. Also, $fy_n(\mu) = ftz_n(\eta) = bz_n(\eta)$, a barycentric subdivision of $z_n(\eta)$ such that for each simplex $\sigma_n$ of $|z_n(\eta)|$, diam $|b\sigma_n| < \nu$. The standard argument for showing that a cycle is homologous to its barycentric subdivision applies here to show that $z_n(\eta) \sim ftz_n(\eta)$ on $Y(\nu)$. But $z_n$ is a n-V-cycle, so $z_n(\eta) \sim z_n(\nu)$ on $Y(\nu)$. Therefore $z_n(\nu) \sim ftz_n(\eta) = fy_n(\mu)$ on $Y(\nu)$.

Thus we have shown that f induces a homomorphism of $H_n^V(X)$ onto $H_n^V(Y)$. To complete the proof, it is only necessary to show that if $fy_n \sim 0$, then $y_n \sim 0$.

Let then $\mu$ be a covering of X, and let $\nu$ be the associated covering of Y, so that $\mu < f^{-1}(\nu)$. Let $\eta = \eta(\mu, \nu)$ and let $\zeta = f^{-1}(\eta)$.

Now recall the sequence $\{\mu_k\}$ of coverings of X constructed in the proof of lemma 2, and choose a common refinement $\delta$ of $\zeta$ and $\mu_0$.

Since $y_n$ is an n-V-cycle, $y_n(\delta) \sim y_n(\zeta)$ on $X(\zeta)$. Hence $fy_n(\delta) \sim fy_n(\zeta)$ on $Y(\eta)$. But if $z_n = fy_n \sim 0$ on Y, then $z_n(\eta) = fy_n(\zeta) \sim 0$ on $Y(\eta)$. Therefore, $fy_n(\delta) \sim 0$ on $Y(\eta)$ and $tfy_n(\delta) \sim 0$ on $X(\mu)$, since t is a chain mapping. We wish now to show that $y_n(\delta) \sim tfy_n(\delta)$ on $X(\mu)$.

Let $L = |y_n(\delta)|$, and let $L \times I$ be considered as a cell complex. Define a chain mapping u on the base and the top of $L \times I$ by $u(\tau_k \times 0) = \tau_k$ and $u(\tau_k \times 1) = tf\tau_k$ for any simplex $\tau_k$ of L. If we now examine the proof of lemma 3, we see that, after substitution of $tf\tau_k$ for $t\sigma_k$ and $\tau_k$ for $t'\sigma_k$, this proof applies without change to show that u can be extended to a chain mapping of all of $L \times I$ into $X(\mu)$. Thus $u(y_n(\delta) \times I)$ is a chain of $X(\mu)$ such that $Fu(y_n(\delta) \times I) = u(y_n(\delta) \times 1) - (y_n(\delta) \times 0) = tfy_n(\delta) - y_n(\delta)$, i.e. $tfy_n(\delta) \sim y_n(\delta)$ on $X(\mu)$.

Now, since $tfy_n(\delta) \sim 0$ on $X(\mu)$, we have $y_n(\delta) \sim 0$ on $X(\mu)$. But $y_n$ is an n-V-cycle so $y_n(\delta) \sim y_n(\mu)$ on $X(\mu)$. Thus $y_n(\mu) \sim 0$ on $X(\mu)$, so $y_n \sim 0$. This completes the proof of theorem 1.

PROOF OF THEOREM 2: Let $\mu$ be a covering of X and y a point of Y. Let $\nu_1 = {}^*\mu$, and let $\varphi$ be the simplicial mapping, defined on p. 34, of $N(\nu_1)$ into $X(\mu)$. We now consider $\nu_1$ as a covering of the compact set $f^{-1}(y)$. Since the coefficient group is an elementary compact group or a field, there is (Steenrod [1, p.678] and Lefschetz [5, p.216]) a refinement $\nu_2$ of $\nu_1$ such that if $z_k$ is a cycle of $N(\nu_2)$ on $f^{-1}(y)$, then $\pi z_k$ is the coordinate on $N(\nu_1)$ of a Čech cycle of $f^{-1}(y)$. Let $\zeta = {}^*\nu_2$. We assert that any cycle $y_k$, $0 \leq k \leq n$, on $X(\zeta)$ $f^{-1}(y)$ bounds on $X(\mu) \cap f^{-1}(y)$.

Let $\Theta$ be the simplicial mapping of $X(\zeta)$ into $N(\nu_2)$ defined on p.34 . Then $\Theta y_k$ is a cycle of $N(\nu_2)$ on $f^{-1}(y)$. Therefore, $\pi\Theta y_k$ is the coordinate on $N(\nu_1)$ of a Čech cycle of $f^{-1}(y)$. Since $H_k^c(f^{-1}(y)) = H_k^v(f^{-1}(y)) = 0$, this Čech cycle bounds and $\pi\Theta y_k \sim 0$ on $N(\nu_1)$. Then $\varphi\pi\Theta y_k \sim 0$ on $X(\mu) \cap f^{-1}(y)$. But it is easy to see, as in the proof that the Čech and Vietoris homology groups are isomorphic, that $\varphi\pi\Theta y_k \sim y_k$ on $X(\mu) \cap f^{-1}(y)$. Now we can choose $\zeta(\mu,y)$ to be $\zeta$, and the hypothesis of theorem 1 is satisfied. This proves theorem 2.

DEFINITIONS (Begle [3] ).

Let K be a finite simplicial complex. A realization of K in $X(\alpha)$ is a chain mapping $\tau$ of K into $X(\alpha)$. If $\beta$ is another covering of X, we write norm $\tau < \beta$ if for each simplex $\sigma$ of K, diam $|\tau\sigma| < \beta$, i.e. if there is a member of $\beta$ which contains the complex $|\tau\sigma|$.

A partial realization $\tau'$ of K is a realization of a subcomplex L of K which contains all the vertices of K. We write norm $\tau' < \beta$ if for each simplex $\sigma$ of K there is a member of $\beta$ which contains all the complexes $|\tau'\sigma'|$ for those faces $\sigma'$ of $\sigma$ which are in L.

A compact Hausdorff space X is lc if for each covering $\varepsilon$ of X there is a refinement $\kappa = \kappa(\varepsilon)$ and for each covering $\beta$ there is a refinement $\alpha = \alpha(\beta, \varepsilon)$ such that if K is a finite simplicial complex and $\tau'$ a partial realization of K in $X(\alpha)$ with norm $\tau' < \kappa$, then there is a realization $\tau$ of K in $X(\beta)$, with norm $\tau < \varepsilon$ and such that $\tau\sigma = \tau'\sigma$ whenever the latter is defined.

We now derive those properties of lc spaces which we need in the statements and proofs of the theorems.

LEMMA 4 (Begle [3]). If X is lc, there is a covering $\nu_0$ of X such that if z is a V-cycle and if $z(\nu) \sim 0$ on $X(\nu)$ for some $\nu < \nu_0$, then $z \sim 0$.

PROOF: Let $\varepsilon$ be the covering consisting of the single open set X, and let $\nu_0 = \kappa(\varepsilon)$. Now suppose $z(\nu) \sim 0$ on $X(\nu)$ for some $\nu < \nu_0$. Let $\nu_1$ be any refinement of $\nu$ and let $\nu_2 = \alpha(\nu_1, \varepsilon)$. Since z is a V-cycle, $z(\nu_2) \sim z(\nu)$ on $X(\nu)$. Therefore, $z(\nu_2) \sim 0$ on $X(\nu)$. Let c be a chain on $X(\nu)$ such that $F(c) = z(\nu_2)$.

We define a partial realization $\tau'$ of $|c|$ in $X(\nu_2)$ by setting $\tau'\sigma = \sigma$ if $\sigma$ is in $|z(\nu_2)|$ or is a vertex of $|c|$. Clearly, norm $\tau' < \nu < \nu_0 = \kappa(\varepsilon)$. Therefore, there is a realization $\tau$ of $|c|$ in $X(\nu_1)$, and $\tau\sigma = \tau'\sigma$ whenever the latter is defined. Thus, $F\tau(c) = \tau F(c) = \tau(z(\nu_2)) = \tau'(z(\nu_2)) = z(\nu_2)$, and so $z(\nu_2) \sim 0$ on $X(\nu_1)$. But $z(\nu_2) \sim z(\nu_1)$ on $X(\nu_1)$, so $z(\nu_1) \sim 0$ on $X(\nu_1)$. Since $\nu_1$ is an arbitrary refinement of $\nu$, this proves the lemma.

LEMMA 5 (Begle [3] ). If X is lc, then its homology groups are isomorphic to the corresponding groups of a finite complex.

PROOF: Let $\nu_0$ be the covering of lemma 4, and let $\nu_1 = {}^*\nu_0$. For each element $U \in \nu_1$, let $\varphi(U)$ be a point in U. Then $\varphi$ is a simplicial mapping of $N(\nu_1)$ into $X(\nu_0)$. Let $K = \varphi[N(\nu_1)]$. K is a finite subcomplex of $X(\nu_0)$. Next, let $\nu_2 = {}^*\nu_1$. For each vertex $x \in X(\nu_2)$, choose an element $V \in \nu_2$ such that $x \in V$ and then choose an element $W \in \nu_1$ such that $St\,(V,\nu_2) \subset W$. Let $\Theta(x) = W$. Then $\Theta$ is a simplicial mapping of $X(\nu_2)$ into $N(\nu_1)$. In the proof of the fact that the Vietoris and Čech homology groups are isomorphic, we have shown that, if $\underline{z}$ is any cycle on $X(\nu_2)$, then $\varphi\Theta(c) \sim \underline{c}$ on $X(\nu_0)$. (See p.35.)

Let z now be a V-cycle of X. Let $w(z) = \varphi\Theta(z(\nu_2))$. Then w induces a homomorphism of $H_n(X)$ into $H_n(K)$, for all $n \geq 0$. We assert that this homomorphism is actually an isomorphism. For if $w(z) = \varphi\Theta(z(\nu_2)) \sim 0$ on K, then $\varphi\Theta(z(\nu_2)) \sim 0$ on $X(\nu_0)$, since $K \subset X(\nu_0)$. But $z(\nu_2) \sim \varphi\Theta(z(\nu_2))$ on $X(\nu_0)$ and $z(\nu_2) \sim z(\nu_0)$ on $X(\nu_0)$, since z is a V-cycle. Thus $z(\nu_0) \sim 0$ on $X(\nu_0)$ and so, by lemma 4, $z \sim 0$. Thus the homology groups of X are isomorphic to subgroups of the homology groups of K, and this proves the lemma.

LEMMA 6 (Begle [3]). If X is lc, then each covering $\mu$ of X has a normal refinement $\mu'$, i.e. a refinement such that, if c is a cycle on $X(\mu')$, then there is a V-cycle z such that $z(\mu) = c$.

PROOF: Let $\varepsilon$ be the covering of X consisting of the single open set X, and let $\varepsilon_1 = \kappa(\varepsilon)$ and $\varepsilon_2 = \kappa({}^*\varepsilon_1)$. It is sufficient to prove the lemma for the case $\mu < \varepsilon_2$. We assert that for any such covering we can choose $\mu'$ to be $\alpha(\mu, {}^*\varepsilon_1)$.

Suppose then that c is a cycle on $X(\mu')$. For each covering $\mu_1 < \mu'$, let $\mu_2 = \alpha(\mu_1, {}^*\varepsilon_1)$, and define a partial realization $\tau'$ of $|c|$ in $X(\mu_2)$ by setting $\tau'\sigma_0 = \sigma_0$ for each vertex $\sigma_0$ of $|c|$. Since $\mu' < \mu < \varepsilon_2 = \kappa({}^*\varepsilon_1)$, norm $\tau' < \kappa({}^*\varepsilon_1)$. Hence there is a realization $\tau$ of $|c|$ in $X(\mu_1)$ with norm $\tau < {}^*\varepsilon_1$. In the special case where $\mu_1 = \mu'$, we can and do choose $\tau$ to be the identity chain mapping.

Now for each refinement $\mu_1$ of $\mu'$, we have a cycle $y(\mu_1) = \tau c$ on $X(\mu_1)$. This collection of cycles does not necessarily form a V-cycle, but it does have the property that if $\nu_1$ and $\nu_2$ are refinements of $\alpha(\mu_1, \varepsilon)$, then $y(\nu_1) \sim y(\nu_2)$ on $X(\mu_1)$. To see that this is so, consider the cartesian product $K = |c| \times I$. We define a partial realization $\rho'$ of K in $X(\alpha(\mu_1, \varepsilon))$ by defining $\rho'$ on the base of K to be the chain mapping $\tau$ from $|c|$ to $X(\nu_1)$ and on the top of K to be the chain mapping from $|c|$ to $X(\nu_2)$. Since the norm of each of these mappings is less than ${}^*\varepsilon_1$, norm $\rho' < \varepsilon_1 = \kappa(\varepsilon)$. Consequently, there is a realization $\rho$ of K in $X(\mu_1)$. Denote by $c_1$ the copy of c in the base of K and by $c_2$ the corresponding copy in the top of K. Then $c_1 \sim c_2$ on K, so $\rho(c_1) \sim \rho(c_2)$ on $X(\mu_1)$. But $\rho(c_1) = y(\nu_1)$ and $\rho(c_2) = y(\nu_2)$, and so $y(\nu_1) \sim y(\nu_2)$ on $X(\mu_1)$.

Now consider the family of all coverings $\xi$ such that $\alpha(\xi,\varepsilon) < \mu$. This is a cofinal family, and so, in defining a V-cycle, it is sufficient to give its coordinates on this family. For each such $\xi$, define $z(\xi)$ to be $y(\alpha(\xi,\varepsilon))$. If we can show that this collection of cycles forms a V-cycle, then we have proved our lemma, for $z(\mu) = y(\alpha(\mu,\varepsilon)) = y(\mu') = c$.

Suppose that $\xi_1 < \xi_2$. Let $\nu_1 = \alpha(\xi_1,\varepsilon)$ and $\nu_2 = \alpha(\xi_2,\varepsilon)$, and let $\nu_3$ be a common refinement of $\nu_1$ and $\nu_2$. Then, by what was shown above, $y(\nu_3) \sim y(\nu_1)$ on $X(\xi_1)$ and $y(\nu_3) \sim y(\nu_2)$ on $X(\nu_2)$. But $X(\xi_1) \subset X(\xi_2)$, so $z(\xi_1) = y(\nu_1) \sim y(\nu_2) = z(\xi_2)$ on $X(\xi_2)$, so $\{z(\xi)\}$ is a V-cycle, and the lemma is proved.

REMARK (Begle [3]). It is clear that an analogous formula holds for Čech cycles. The interest in this remark lies in the fact that the proof of this lemma holds for any coefficient group. Therefore, in an lc space, any covering has a normal refinement no matter what the coefficient group is.

THEOREM 3 (Begle [3]). Let X be a compact lc space which is acyclic. Let $\mathcal{C}(X)$ denote the family of closed, acyclic subsets of X, and let $f : X \to \mathcal{C}(X)$ be upper semi-continuous. Then there exists a point $x_0 \in X$ such that $x_0 \in f(x_0)$.

Theorem 3 is derived from a more general theorem, a generalization of Lefschetz's fixed point theorem (Lefschetz [5]) which also includes theorem EM2 (p.30) of Eilenberg and Montgomery [1]. Consider a compact space X which is lc (but not necessarily acyclic), and an upper semi-continuous mapping f as above. Let $Y = \{(x,x') \in X \times X \mid x' \in f(x)\}$. Since f is upper semi-continuous, Y is a closed subset of $X \times X$ and hence is compact. We define two mappings $g,h : Y \to X$ by $g(x,x') = x$ and $h(x,x') = x'$, for all $(x,x') \in Y$. Clearly, $f = hg^{-1}$.

For each x in X, $g^{-1}(x)$ is homeomorphic to $f(x)$, which is acyclic. Since the coefficient group is a field, theorem 2 applies to show that g induces an isomorphism $g_{*r} : H_r(Y) \longrightarrow H_r(X)$ onto, for $r \geq 0$. Therefore, $g_{*r}^{-1}$ is an isomorphism defined on $H_r(X)$. Since $h : Y \longrightarrow X$ is continuous, it induces a homomorphism $h_{*r} : H_r(Y) \longrightarrow H_r(X)$, $r \geq 0$. Thus, $h_{*r}\, g_{*r}^{-1} : H_r(X) \longrightarrow H_r(X)$ is a homomorphism. By lemma 5, $H_r(X)$ has a finite basis, and hence the trace of $h_{*r}\, g_{*r}^{-1}$ is defined. Let $\Lambda(f) = \Lambda(g,h) = \sum_{j=0}^{\infty} (-1)^r$ trace $h_{*r}\, g_{*r}^{-1}$. By lemma 5, $H_r(X) = 0$ for sufficiently large r, and so $\Lambda(f)$ exists. We now state

THEOREM 4 (Begle [3]). Let X be a compact lc space. Let $\mathcal{C}(X)$ denote the family of closed, acyclic subsets of X, and let $f : X \longrightarrow \mathcal{C}(X)$ be upper semi-continuous. If $\Lambda(f) \neq 0$, then there exists a point $x_0 \in X$ such that $x_0 \in f(x_0)$.

It is easy to derive theorem 3 from theorem 4. For, if X is acyclic, then $H_r(X) = 0$ for $r > 0$, and $H_0(Y)$ has just one generator, so $\Lambda(f) = 1$ and theorem 2 applies.

PROOF OF THEOREM 4: In order to prove theorem 4, we need an explicit method for calculating $\Lambda(f)$ in terms of the V-cycles of X. We obtain this by first recalling how the mappings g and h of Y into X induce the homomorphisms $g_{*r}$ and $h_{*r}$ of $H_r(Y)$ into $H_r(X)$.

Let z be an r-V-cycle of X. For each covering $\mu$ of Y, choose a covering $\nu$ of X such that $\mu < g^{-1}(\nu)$, and if $\mu = g^{-1}(\nu)$ for some $\nu$, choose this $\nu$. Let $y(\mu) = tz(\eta)$, where $\eta = \eta(\mu,\nu)$ is the refinement of $\nu$ given by lemma 2, and t is the corresponding chain mapping of $X(\eta)$ into $Y(\mu)$. Then, as was shown in the proof of theorem 2, $y = \{y(\mu)\}$ is an r-V-cycle of Y, which we now denote by $g_r^{-1}(z)$, and the transformation $z \longrightarrow g_r^{-1}(z)$ induces precisely the isomorphism $g_{*r}^{-1} : H_r(X) \longrightarrow H_r(X)$.

It appears at a first glance that $y = g_r^{-1}(z)$ depends on the order of g as a Vietoris mapping, since the construction of $\eta(\mu,\nu)$ in the proof of lemma 2, depends on the order of g. However, the homology class of y is independent of this order, since the homomorphism $g_{*r} : H_r(Y) \longrightarrow H_r(X)$ determined by g is uniquely defined. Therefore, in the above construction, we may take g to be of any convenient order $k \geq r$.

Next, given any r-V-cycle y of Y, for any covering $\nu$ of Y, let $\mu = h^{-1}(\nu)$, and let $z(\nu) = h(y(\mu))$. Then $z = \{z(\nu)\}$ is an r-V-cycle of X, which we denote by $h_r(y)$, and the transformation

$y \longrightarrow h_r(y)$ induces the homomorphism $h_{*r} : H_r(Y) \longrightarrow H_r(X)$.

Thus the transformation $z \longrightarrow h_r g_r^{-1}(z)$, where z is an r-V-cycle of X, induces the homomorphism $h_{*r} g_{*r}^{-1} : H_r(X) \longrightarrow H_r(X)$. Let $z_1, z_2, \ldots, z_k$ be a homology basis for the r-V-cycles of X, i.e. a maximal set of r-V-cycles which are independent with respect to homology. Then, for each integer i, $1 \le i \le k$, $h_r g_r^{-1}(z_i) \sim \sum a_{ij}^r z_j$. But now $\Lambda(f) = \Lambda(g,h) = \sum_{r \ge 0} (-1)^r \operatorname{trace}(a_{ij}^r) = \sum_{r \ge 0} \sum_{i=1}^{k} (-1)^r a_{ii}^r$.

Next we show that the calculation of $\Lambda(f)$ can be reduced to a similar calculation for a chain mapping of a finite complex into itself.

Let $\varepsilon$ be an arbitrary covering of X, and let $\varepsilon_1 = {}^*\kappa(\varepsilon)$ and $\varepsilon_2 = \kappa(\varepsilon_1)$, where the notation refers to the definition of an lc space. Let $\nu$ be a common refinement of $\varepsilon_2$ and of the covering $\nu_o$ of lemma 4, and let K be the finite subcomplex $\varphi[N({}^*\nu)]$ of $X(\nu)$.

We are going to define a chain mapping $v : K \longrightarrow K$. Before doing this, we note that if z is an r-V-cycle of X, then the coordinate of $h_r g_r^{-1}(z)$ is obtained by first choosing a covering $\nu_1$ such that $\mu_1 < g^{-1}(\nu_1)$, where $\mu_1 = h^{-1}(\nu)$. Then $h_r g_r^{-1}(z(\nu)) = ht_1(z(\eta_1))$, where $\eta_1 = \eta(\mu_1, \nu_1)$. Recall that $\eta_1$ depends on the order of the Vietoris mapping g. Choose an integer which is greater than the dimension of K and which is such that the homology groups of X for dimensions greater than this integer are all zero. Take this to be the order of g in constructing $\eta_1$, and in the construction of $\eta_2$ below.

To define the chain mapping v, set $\nu' = {}^{**}\nu$, and choose a normal refinement $\nu_2$ of $\nu'$ (lemma 6). Let $\mu_2 = h^{-1}(\nu_2)$, and $\eta_2 = \eta(\mu_2, \nu_2)$. Since $\nu_2 < \nu$, $\mu_2 < \mu_1$. Therefore, by lemma 3, there is a common refinement $\lambda_1$ of $\eta_1$ and $\eta_2$ such that $t_1(x) \sim t_2(x)$ on $Y(\mu_1)$ for any cycle x of $X(\lambda_1)$, where $t_1 : X(\eta_1) \longrightarrow Y(\mu_1)$ and $t_2 : X(\eta_2) \longrightarrow Y(\mu_2)$ are the chain mappings of lemma 3. Let $\lambda_2 = \alpha(\lambda_1, \varepsilon)$.

Now let $\tau'$ be the identity mapping of the null-skeleton of K, so that $\tau'$ is a partial realization of K in $Y(\lambda_3)$, where $\lambda_3 = \alpha(\lambda_2, \varepsilon_1)$. Since $\nu < \varepsilon_2 = \kappa(\varepsilon_1)$, norm $\tau' < \kappa(\varepsilon_1)$. Hence there is a realization $\tau : K \longrightarrow X(\lambda_2)$ of norm $< \varepsilon_1$, and such that for each vertex $\sigma_0$ of K, we have $\tau\sigma_0 = \tau'\sigma_0 = \sigma_0$.

Since $\lambda_2 < \lambda_1$, $t_2$ is defined on $X(\lambda_2)$, so $t_2\tau : K \to Y(\mu_2)$ is a chain mapping, and $ht_2\tau : K \to X(\nu_2) \subset X(\nu')$ is a chain mapping. Let $\pi$ denote the transformation $\varphi\Theta : X(\nu') \to K$. Define the chain mapping v to be $\pi h t_2 \tau$.

Let $\Lambda(v) = \sum_{r \geq 0} (-1)^r$ trace $v_{*r}$, where $v_{*r} : H_r(K) \to H_r(K)$ is the homomorphism induced by v. We now assert that trace $h_{*r}g_{*r}^{-1}$ = trace $v_{*r}$ for each $r \geq 0$, and hence that $\Lambda(f) = \Lambda(v)$. To prove this, let $z_1, \ldots, z_k$ be a homology basis for the r-cycles of X. These cycles may be chosen such that, for each i, $z_i(\nu) = \varphi\Theta z_i(\nu')$ of K. For, $z_i(\nu') \sim z_i(\nu)$ on $X(\nu)$, since $z_i$ is a V-cycle. Also, $\varphi\Theta(z_i(\nu')) \sim z_i(\nu')$ on $X(\nu)$. Hence, if the coordinate $z_i(\nu)$ of $z_i$ is replaced by $\varphi\Theta(z_i(\nu'))$, the resulting V-cycle is homologous to the original one.

Now we construct a homology basis for the r-cycles of K. Let $\varphi\Theta(z_i(\nu')) = c_i$. Since the cycles $z_1, \ldots, z_k$ are independent on X, and since $\nu$ is a refinement of the covering $\nu_0$ of lemma 4, the coordinates $c_1, \ldots, c_k$ are independent on $X(\nu)$ and hence on K. Therefore, a homology basis for K can be obtained by adding independent cycles $c_{k+1}, \ldots, c_l$ to the set $c_1, \ldots, c_k$.

Since v is a chain mapping, $v(x_i)$ is an r-cycle on K $(1 \leq i \leq l)$, and so $v(x_i) \sim \sum_{j=1}^{l} b_{ij}^r x_j$. Now trace $(b_{ij}^r) = \sum_{i=1}^{l} b_{ii}^r$, so we have to show that $\sum_{i=1}^{k} a_{ii}^r = \sum_{i=1}^{l} b_{ii}^r$.

We first show that $b_{ij}^r = 0$ for $k+1 \leq i \leq l$. Recall that $ht_2\tau x_i$ is a cycle of $X(\nu_2)$ $(1 \leq i \leq l)$. By the choice of $\nu_2$, there is an r-V-cycle $z_i'$ such that $z_i'(\nu') = ht_2\tau(x_i)$. Since $z_1, \ldots, z_k$ forms a homology basis, $z_i' \sim \sum_{j=1}^{k} c_{ij}^r z_j$ and so $ht_2\tau(x_i) = z_i'(\nu)$ $\sim \sum_{j=1}^{k} c_{ij}^r z(\nu')$ on $X(\nu')$. Therefore

$$\pi h t_2\tau(x_i) \sim \sum_{j=1}^{k} c_{ij}^r \pi z_j(\nu') = \sum_{j=1}^{k} c_{ij}^r x_j \quad \text{on K.}$$

Thus, $v(x_i)$ $(1 \leq i \leq l)$ is linearly dependent on the first k elements of the homology basis for K. Therefore, the last l-k columns of matrix $(b_{ij}^r)$ consist of zeros, and trace $(b_{ij}^r) = \sum_{i=1}^{k} b_{ii}^r$.

To finish the proof of our assertion, it is sufficient to show that $b_{ij}^r = a_{ij}^r$ for $i,j = 1, \ldots, k$. To do this, consider any cycle

$x_i$ $(i=1,\ldots,k)$, and let $z_i'$ be the r-V-cycle defined above such that $z_i'(v') = ht_2\tau(x_i)$. Let $z_i''$ be the r-V-cycle $h_r g_r^{-1}(z_i)$.

We wish to prove that $z_i' \sim z_i''$. By lemma 4, it is sufficient to show that $z_i'(v) \sim z_i''(v)$ on $X(v)$. We start by proving that $z_i(\lambda_2) \sim \tau x_i$ on $X(\lambda_1)$. Since $z_i$ is a V-cycle, $z_i(\lambda_2) \sim z_i(v) = x_i$ on $X(v)$. Let c be a chain of $X(v)$ such that $F(c) = z_i(\lambda_2) - x_i$. Define a partial realization $\rho'$ of $|c|$ into $X(\lambda_2)$ by letting $\rho' = \tau$ on $|x_i|$ and the identity on $|z_i(\lambda_2)|$ and on the vertices of $|c| \setminus (|z_i(\lambda_2)| \cup |x_i|)$. Since norm $\tau < \varepsilon_1 = {}^*\kappa(\varepsilon)$, and since $v < \varepsilon_1$, norm $\rho' < \kappa(\varepsilon)$. Also, $\lambda_2 = \alpha(\lambda_1, \varepsilon)$. Therefore, there is a realization $\rho\colon |c| \to X(\lambda_1)$ with norm $\rho < \varepsilon$. Now $F\rho(c) = \rho F(c) = = \rho(z_i(\lambda_2)) - \tau x_i$, since $\rho = \rho'$ whenever $\rho'$ is defined. Thus $z_i(\lambda_2) \sim \tau x_i$ on $X(\lambda_1)$.

Since $t_2$ is a chain mapping, $t_2(z_i(\lambda_2)) \sim t_2 \tau x_i$ on $Y(\mu_2)$. By the choice of $\lambda_1$, $t_2(z_i(\lambda_2)) \sim t_1(z_i(\lambda_2))$ on $Y(\mu_1)$, and since $Y(\mu_2) \subset Y(\mu_1)$, we have $t_2\tau(x_i) \sim t_1(z_i(\lambda_2))$ on $Y(\mu_1)$. Also, since $\lambda_2 < \eta_1$, $z_i(\lambda_2) \sim z_i(\eta_1)$ on $X(\eta_1)$ and so $t_1(z_i(\lambda_2)) \sim t_1(z_i(\eta_1))$ on $Y(\mu_1)$. Since h is a simplicial mapping, $ht_2\tau(x_i) \sim ht_1(z_i(\eta_1))$ on $X(v)$.

But $ht_1(z_i(\eta_1)) = z_i''(v)$ and $ht_2\,\tau(x_i) = z_i'(v')$. Since $z_i'(v') \sim z_i'(v)$ on $X(v)$, $z_i'(v) \sim z_i''(v)$ and hence $z_i' \sim z_i''$.

Now since $z_i'' = h_r g_r^{-1}(z_i) \sim \sum_{j=1}^{k} a_{ij}^r z_j$, we have

$$z_i' \sim \sum_{j=1}^{k} a_{ij}^r z_j \text{ and } z_i'(v') \sim ht_2\tau(x_i) \sim \sum_{j=1}^{k} a_{ij}^r z_j(v') \text{ on } X(v').$$

Consequently,

$$\pi ht_2\tau(x_i) = v(x_i) \sim \sum_{j=1}^{k} a_{ij}^r \pi(z_j(v')) = \sum_{j=1}^{k} a_{ij}^r \text{ on } K.$$

But

$$v(x_i) \sim \sum_{j=1}^{k} b_{ij}^r x_j, \text{ so } a_{ij}^r = b_{ij}^r \quad (i,j=1,\ldots,k).$$

This completes the proof of the assertion that $\Lambda(f) = \Lambda(v)$.

Finally, since K is a finite complex and since the coefficient group is a field, there is another method for calculating $\Lambda(v)$ and hence $\Lambda(f)$. For each r-simplex $\sigma_r$ of K, let $d_{ij}^r$ be the coefficient of $\sigma_r^j$ in the chain $v(\sigma_r^i)$. Let $\Lambda'(v) = \sum_{r \geq 0} (-1)^r \operatorname{trace} d_{ij}^r$. Then $\Lambda(v) = \Lambda'(v)$ (Lefschetz [5, p.193]).

We are now ready to prove theorem 4. Suppose that $x \notin f(x)$ for all $x \in X$. Then there is a covering $\varepsilon_0$ of X such that $St(x, \varepsilon_0) \cap St(f(x), \varepsilon_0) = \emptyset$ for all $x \in X$. We now specify the covering $\varepsilon$ involved in the definition of K to be this covering $\varepsilon_0$.

Let $\sigma$ be any simplex of K. By construction, $\tau(\sigma)$ is a chain of $X(\lambda_2)$ such that diam $|\tau(\sigma)| < \varepsilon_1 < \varepsilon$. Choose an arbitrary simplex $\sigma'$ of $X(\lambda_2)$ in $|\tau(\sigma)|$, and let x be a vertex of $\sigma'$. Then $\sigma \subset St(x, \varepsilon)$. By the construction of $t_2$, in the proof of lemma 2, $t_2(x) \in g^{-1}(x)$, and also $|t_2(\sigma')| \subset St(g^{-1}(x), \mu_2)$. Therefore, $ht_2(x) \in hg^{-1}(x) = f(x)$ and, since $\mu_2 = h^{-1}(\nu_2)$, $|ht_2(\sigma)| \subset St(f(x), \nu_2)$ and so $|\Pi ht_2(\sigma')| \subset St(f(x), \nu) \subset St(f(x), \varepsilon)$. Since $\sigma \subset St(x, \varepsilon)$, $\sigma$ does not meet any simplex of $\Pi ht_2(\sigma')$. But $\sigma'$ was an arbitrary simplex of $|\tau(\sigma)|$, so $\sigma$ does not meet any simplex of $\Pi ht_2 \tau(\sigma) = v(\sigma)$. Thus, for every r and i, $d^r_{ii} = 0$ and so $\Lambda'(v) = 0$. But $\Lambda'(g) = \Lambda(g) = \Lambda(f) \neq 0$, and so the assumption, that $x \notin f(x)$ for all $x \in X$, leads to a contradiction.

In 1961 Fan [3], using convexity arguments, obtained results which generalize the fixed point theorem of Tychonoff [1], but they neither include Kakutani's theorem (Kakutani [2]), nor are they included in the generalizations of Kakutani's theorem by Bohnenblust and Karlin [1], Fan [1], Glicksberg [1] and Begle [3]. Fan's results do not invoke any known fixed point theorem, and they are all derived directly from the theorem of Knaster - Kuratowski - Mazurkiewicz [1], which was used in their well-known proof of Brouwer's theorem. The Knaster - Kuratowski - Mazurkiewicz theorem is reformulated in the following generalized form:

LEMMA 7 (Fan [3]). Let X be a subset of a topological linear space Y. For each $x \in X$, let a closed subset F(x) of Y be given such that the following conditions are satisfied:

(i) The convex hull of any finite subset $\{x_1, x_2, \ldots, x_n\}$ of X is contained in $\bigcup_{i=1}^{n} F(x_i)$.

(ii) F(x) is compact for at least one $x \in X$.

Then $\cap\{F(x) \mid x \in X\} \neq \emptyset$.

PROOF: Because of condition (ii), it suffices to show that $\bigcap_{i=1}^{n} F(x_i) \neq \emptyset$ for any finite subset $\{x_1, x_2, \ldots, x_n\}$ of X. Given $\{x_1, x_2, \ldots, x_n\} \subset X$, consider the closed (n-1)-simplex

$S = (v_1, v_2, \ldots, v_n)$ in $E^n$ with vertices $v_1 = (1,0,\ldots,0)$, $v_2 = (0,1,0,\ldots,0), \ldots, v_n = (0,0,0,\ldots,1)$, and define a continuous mapping $\varphi: S \to Y$ by $\varphi(\sum_{i=1}^{n} \alpha_i v_i) = \sum_{i=1}^{n} \alpha_i x_i$ for $\alpha_i \geq 0$, $\sum_{i=1}^{n} \alpha_i = 1$. Consider the n closed subsets $G_i = \varphi^{-1}[F(x_i)]$ $(i=1,2,\ldots,n)$ of S. By (i), for any indices $1 \leq i_1 < i_2 < \ldots < i_k \leq n$, the (k-1)-simplex $(v_{i_1}, v_{i_2}, \ldots, v_{i_k})$ is contained in $\bigcup_{j=1}^{k} G_{i_j}$. According to the Knaster - Kuratowski - Mazurkiewicz theorem, this implies that $\bigcap_{i=1}^{n} G_i \neq \emptyset$, and so $\bigcap_{i=1}^{n} F(x_i) \neq \emptyset$.

Let Z be a topological group and let $\mathcal{C}(Z)$ be the family of all non-empty compact subsets of Z. $\mathcal{C}(Z)$ is topologized as follows: For $A \in \mathcal{C}(Z)$ and for each neighbourhood V of the identity e of Z, let $\tilde{V}(A) = \{B \in \mathcal{C}(Z) \mid B \subset AV,\ A \subset BV\}$. The family of all sets of the form $\tilde{V}(A)$, where V runs through the neighbourhoods of e, is taken as a basis for the neighbourhood system of A in $\mathcal{C}(Z)$.

Let X be a topological space, and Z a topological group. With $\mathcal{C}(Z)$ topologized as above, a mapping $f : X \to \mathcal{C}(Z)$ is continuous if and only if, for any $x_o \in X$ and any neighbourhood V of $e \in Z$, there is a neighbourhood U of $x_o$ in X such that $f(x) \subset f(x_o).V$ and $f(x_o) \subset f(x).V$ for all $x \in U$. In the remainder of this chapter a transformation $g : X \to \mathcal{C}(Z)$ will be called <u>upper semi-continuous</u> if and only if, for any $x_o \in X$ and for any neighbourhood V of $e \in Z$, there is a neighbourhood U of $x_o$ in X such that $g(x) \subset g(x_o).V$ for all $x \in U$. (When Z is compact, this definition of upper semi-continuity coincides with the one given on p.14.)

LEMMA 8 (Fan [3] ). Let X be a topological space and Z a topological group. Let $f,g : X \to \mathcal{C}(Z)$ be upper semi-continuous. If F is a non-empty closed subset of Z, then

$$E = \{x \in X \mid F.f(x) \cap g(x) \neq \emptyset\}$$

is closed in X.

PROOF: Take $x_o \in X \setminus E$. Since $f(x_o)$ is compact and F is closed, $F.f(x_o)$ is closed. Since the compact set $g(x_o)$ is disjoint from the closed set $F.f(x_o)$, there is a neighbourhood V of $e \in Z$ such that $F.f(x_o).V \cap g(x_o).V = \emptyset$. Choose a neighbourhood U of $x_o$ in X such that $f(x) \subset f(x_o).V$ and $g(x) \subset g(x_o).V$ for all $x \in U$. Then for

$x \in U$ we have $F.f(x) \cap g(x) = \emptyset$, i.e. $x \in X \setminus E$ for $x \in U$. Hence E is closed in X.

LEMMA 9 Fan [3]). Let X be a topological space and Z a topological group. Let $f : X \to \mathcal{C}(Z)$ be continuous. If G is an open subset of Z, then

$$H = \{x \in X \mid f(x) \cap G = \emptyset\}$$

is closed in X.

PROOF: Take $x_0 \in X \setminus H$, and $z \in f(x_0) \cap G$. Then $V = G^{-1}z$ is a neighbourhood of e in Z. Choose a neighbourhood U of $x_0$ in X such that $f(x_0) \subset f(x).V$ for all $x \in U$. Then for each $x \in U$, $z \in f(x_0) \subset f(x).V$, so $f(x) \cap zV^{-1} \neq \emptyset$, i.e. $f(x) \cap G \neq \emptyset$. Thus $H \cap U = \emptyset$ and H is closed in X.

THEOREM 5 (Fan [3]). Let X be a compact convex subset of a topological linear space Y. Let Z be a topological group and let $\mathcal{C}(Z)$ be the family of all non-empty compact subsets of Z, topologized as above. Let $f : X \to \mathcal{C}(Z)$ be continuous and $g : X \to \mathcal{C}(Z)$ be upper semi-continuous, such that the following conditions are fulfilled:

(i) For each $x' \in X$, there is an $x'' \in X$ such that $f(x') \cap g(x'') \neq \emptyset$.

(ii) Given any neighbourhood of the identity $e \in Z$, there is a neighbourhood W of e with the following property: For every point $x_0 \in X$ and for any finite subset $\{x_1, x_2, \ldots, x_n\}$ of X, the relations $W.f(x_0) \cap g(x_i) \neq \emptyset$ $(i=1,\ldots,n)$ imply $V.f(x_0) \cap g(x) \neq \emptyset$, for any point x in the convex hull of $\{x_1, \ldots, x_n\}$.

Then there exists a point $\hat{x} \in X$ such that $f(\hat{x}) \cap g(\hat{x}) \neq \emptyset$.

PROOF: Let $\mathcal{U}$ denote the family of all neighbourhoods of $e \in Z$. For each $V \in \mathcal{U}$, let

$$\varphi(V) = \{x \in X \mid \bar{V}.f(x) \cap g(x) \neq \emptyset\}.$$

By lemma 8, $\varphi(V)$ is closed in X. If we can prove that $\varphi(V) \neq \emptyset$ for every $V \in \mathcal{U}$, then it will follow that

$$\bigcap_{i=1}^{n} \varphi(V_i) \supset \varphi(\bigcap_{i=1}^{n} V_i) \neq \emptyset$$

for any finite number of members $V_1, V_2, \ldots, V_n$ of $\mathcal{U}$. The compactness of X will then imply that $\cap\{\varphi(V) \mid V \in \mathcal{U}\} \neq \emptyset$. Since every point $\hat{x} \in \cap \{\varphi(V) | V \in \mathcal{U}\}$ satisfies $f(\hat{x}) \cap g(\hat{x}) \neq \emptyset$, it remains to show that $\varphi(V) \neq \emptyset$ for every $V \in \mathcal{U}$.

Consider an arbitrary fixed $V \in \mathcal{U}$. For this V, choose a $W \in \mathcal{U}$ with the property stated in (ii) of the theorem. For each $x \in X$, let

$$F(x) = \varphi(V) \cup \{ y \in X | W.f(y) \cap g(x) = \emptyset \}.$$

Since $W.f(y) \cap g(x) = \emptyset$ is equivalent to $f(y) \cap W^{-1}.g(x) = \emptyset$ and $W^{-1}g(x)$ is open, $\{y \in X | W.f(y) \cap g(x) = \emptyset\}$ is closed, by lemma 9. Hence F(x) is compact. We claim that $\sum_{i=1}^{n} \alpha_i x_i \in \bigcup_{i=1}^{n} F(x_i)$ for any finite subset $\{x_1, x_2, \ldots, x_n\}$ of X and for any $\alpha_i \geq 0$ with $\sum_{i=1}^{n} \alpha_i = 1$. In fact, if $\sum_{j=1}^{n} \alpha_j x_j \notin \varphi(V)$, then $V.f(\sum \alpha_j x_j) \cap g(\sum \alpha_j x_j) = \emptyset$; so, by our choice of W, for at least one index i, we have $W.f(\sum \alpha_j x_j) \cap g(x_i) = \emptyset$ and therefore $\sum \alpha_j x_j \in F(x_i)$. By lemma 7, there is an $x' \in \cap \{F(x) | x \in X\}$. By (i), we can choose $x'' \in X$ such that $f(x') \cap g(x'') \neq \emptyset$. Then $W.f(x') \cap g(x'') \neq \emptyset$ and $x' \in F(x'')$ imply $x' \in \varphi(V)$. Hence $\varphi(V) \neq 0$ and the theorem is proved.

When g is a continuous mapping of X into Z, it may be considered (in an obvious way) as an upper semi-continuous mapping $g : X \rightarrow \mathcal{C}(Z)$. In this case, condition (ii) of theorem 5 may be restated as follows: Given any neighbourhood V of the identity $e \in Z$, there is a neighbourhood W of e such that, for every $x_0 \in X$, the convex hull of $g^{-1}[W.f(x_0)]$ is contained in $g^{-1}[V.f(x_0)]$.

THEOREM 6 (Fan [3]). Let X be a compact convex subset of a topological linear space Y. Let Z be a locally convex topological linear space and let $\mathcal{K}(Z)$ be the subfamily of $\mathcal{C}(Z)$ consisting of all non-empty compact convex subsets of Z. Let $f : X \rightarrow \mathcal{K}(Z)$ be continuous with respect to the relative topology of $\mathcal{K}(Z)$ induced by the topology of $\mathcal{C}(Z)$, and let $g : X \rightarrow Z$ be continuous. Let f and g satisfy the following conditions:

(i) $f(x) \cap g[X] \neq \emptyset$ for every $x \in X$.

(ii) For every closed convex subset C of Z, $g^{-1}[C]$ is convex (or empty).

Then there exists a point $\hat{x} \in X$ such that $g(\hat{x}) \in f(\hat{x})$.

PROOF: By the local convexity and regularity of Z, for any neighbourhood V of the null-element of Z, we can find a convex neighbourhood W of the null-element of Z such that $\overline{W} \subset V$. Then, for any $x_o \in X$, $\bar{W} + f(x_o)$ is closed and convex, and therefore, by (ii), $g^{-1}[\bar{W} + f(x_o)]$ is convex. $g^{-1}[V + f(x_o)]$ contains the convex set $g^{-1}[\bar{W} + f(x_o)]$, which contains the convex hull of $g^{-1}[W + f(x_o)]$. Thus condition (ii) of theorem 5 is satisfied (see the remark preceding theorem 6).

COROLLARY. If $f : X \to X$ is continuous and $g : X \to X$ is the identity mapping, theorem 6 reduces to the fixed point theorem of Tychonoff [1].

We now replace the topological group in theorem 5 by a uniform space Z, but we consider continuous mappings $f, g : X \to Z$ only.

THEOREM 7 (Fan [3]). Let X be a compact convex subset of a topological linear space Y, and let Z be a uniform space. Let $\mathscr{C}(Z)$ denote the family of all non-empty compact subsets of Z. Let $f, g : X \to Z$ be continuous mappings satisfying the following conditions:

(i) $f[X] \subset g[X]$

(ii) For any entourage V of Z, there is an entourage W of Z such that for any $z \in f[X]$, any finite subset $\{x_1, x_2, \ldots, x_n\}$ of X and for any $\alpha_i \geq 0$ $(i=1,2,\ldots,n)$ with $\sum_{i=1}^{n} \alpha_i = 1$, the relations $(z, g(x_i)) \in W$ $(i=1,2,\ldots,n)$ imply $(z, g(\sum_{i=1}^{n} \alpha_i x_i)) \in V$.

Then there exists a point $\hat{x} \in X$ such that $g(\hat{x}) = f(\hat{x})$.

PROOF: The proof is similar to that of theorem 5. Let $\mathcal{U}$ denote the family of all those entourages of Z which are open in $Z \times Z$. For each $V \in \mathcal{U}$, let

$$\varphi(V) = \{x \in X \mid (f(x), g(x)) \in \bar{V}\}$$

where $\bar{V}$ denotes the closure of Z in $Z \times Z$. $\varphi(V)$ is closed in X : $\varphi(V) = f^{-1}[\bar{V}(g(x))]$, where $\bar{V}(g(x)) = \{y \in X \mid (g(x), y) \in \bar{V}\}$. The theorem will be proved, if we can show that $\varphi(V) \neq \emptyset$ for every $V \in \mathcal{U}$.

For any fixed $V \in \mathcal{U}$, choose a $W \in \mathcal{U}$ with the property described in condition (ii). For each $x \in X$, let

$$F(x) = \varphi(V) \cup \{y \in X \mid (f(y), g(x)) \notin W\}.$$

Since W is open in $Z \times Z$, $\{y \in X \mid (f(y), g(x)) \notin W\}$ is closed in X. Hence F(x) is compact. By lemma 7, there is a point

$x' \in \cap \{F(x) | x \in X\}$ . Let $x'' \in X$ be such that $f(x') = g(x'')$. Then from $x' \in F(x'')$ it follows that $x' \in \varphi(V)$.

Again, theorem 7 generalizes Tychonoff's fixed point theorem. In fact, when $Y = Z$ is a locally convex topological linear space and g is the identity on X, condition (ii) of theorem 7 follows immediately from the local convexity.

## 1.4. Multi-valued mappings such that the image of each point is non-acyclic

In this section, if X is a topological space, then $\mathcal{C}(X)$ will denote the family of non-empty closed subsets of X.

Hamilton [2] (1947) considered multi-valued mappings for which the image of a point was supposed connected, but not acyclic. Let $C^n$ be an n-cell in $E^n$ $(n \geq 2)$, and let f be a mapping such that for each $x \in C^n$, $f(x)$ is the boundary (n-1)-sphere of an n-cell in $C^n$. Then Hamilton [2] asserted that there exists a fixed point if either

(i) f is continuous (i.e. f is upper semi-continuous and lower semi-continuous );or

(ii) f is upper semi-continuous and there is an $\varepsilon > 0$ such that for each $x \in C^n$, the interior domain of $f(x)$ contains an $\varepsilon$-neighbourhood in $E^n$.

However, Capel and Strother [2] (1957) and O'Neill [2] (1957), gave counter-examples to the first of these assertions. Hamilton [2] (1957) showed that the second assertion was valid, and this is confirmed by the following theorem of O'Neill [2] , of which it is a corollary:

1. (O'Neill [2]). Let X be an ANR in $E^n$, and let $f : X \longrightarrow \mathcal{C}(X)$ satisfy the following conditions:

(i) If $x \in X$ and U is a neighbourhood of $f(x)$, there is a neighbourhood V of x such that if $y \in V$ then $f(y) \subset U$ (i.e. f is upper semi-continuous), and each (n-1)-cycle on $f(x)$ is homologous in U to a cycle on $f(y)$ (augmented Čech homology with a field of coefficients);

(ii) If $x \in X$ and $0 \leq r \leq n-2$, then $H_r(f(x)) = 0$.

Then X has a fixed point under f.

O'Neill [3] (1957) defined induced homology homomorphisms for multi-valued mappings and used it to define a Lefschetz number for mappings under which the image of each point is disconnected. Let H again denote Čech homology theory with coefficients in a field. All spaces are assumed to be compact metric. Thus the group H(X) can be based on a group C(X) of projective chains (Lefschetz [5, pp.229, 231]). Define the <u>support of a coordinate</u> $c_i$ of $c \in C(X)$ to be the union of the closures of the kernels of the simplexes appearing in $c_i$ (Lefschetz [5, p.245]). Then the intersection of the supports of the coordinates of c is defined to be the <u>support</u> $|c|$ of c. Let A and B be chain groups with supports in the compacta X and Y respectively, and let $\varepsilon > 0$ be given. Let $\varepsilon$ also denote the set-valued function defined by $\varepsilon(x) = \{x' \in X \mid \rho(x,x') \leq \varepsilon\}$, for all $x \in X$, where $\rho$ denotes the metric of X. A chain mapping $\varphi: A \to B$ is <u>accurate</u> with respect to a function $f : X \to \mathcal{C}(Y)$ provided that $|\varphi(a)| \subset f[|a|]$ for each $a \in A$. Further, $\varphi$ is <u>$\varepsilon$-accurate</u> with respect to f provided $\varphi$ is accurate with respect to the composite function $\varepsilon f \varepsilon$.

A homomorphism $h : H(X) \to H(Y)$ is an <u>induced homomorphism</u> of $f : X \to \mathcal{C}(Y)$ provided that, given $\varepsilon > 0$, there is a chain mapping $\varphi: C(X) \to C(Y)$ such that $\varphi$ is $\varepsilon$-accurate with respect to f, and $h = \varphi_*$, where $\varphi_*$ is the homomorphism induced by $\varphi$.

The set of all induced homomorphisms of an arbitrary function $f : X \to \mathcal{C}(Y)$ is a vector space under the usual operations. If $h_f$ and $h_g$ are induced homomorphisms of upper semi-continuous mappings $f : X \to \mathcal{C}(Z)$, and $g : Y \to \mathcal{C}(Z)$, then $h_g h_f$ is an induced homomorphism of gf. If $f : X \to Y$ is a (single-valued) continuous mapping of a connected compactum into a compact polyhedron (for the latter, see Lefschetz [5, pp.94, 308]), then the induced homology homomorphisms of f are exactly the scalar multiples of the Čech homology homomorphism $f_*$ (O'Neill [3]).

A homology homomorphism h is <u>non-trivial</u> provided that the zero-dimensional component $h_0 : H_0(X) \to H_0(Y)$ is not the zero homomorphism.

We now have

2. (O'Neill [3]). Let X be a compact polyhedron, $f : X \to \mathcal{C}(X)$ upper semi-continuous and $h : H(X) \to H(X)$ the induced homology homomorphism of f. Then the Lefschetz number $\Lambda(h) = \sum(-1)^r$ trace

$h_r$ can be formed, and if $\Lambda(h) \neq 0$, then X has a fixed point under f.

To be able to use this fact, it is necessary to produce an induced homology homomorphism of f, which maps some r-cycle non-trivially ($r \geq 0$).

3. (O'Neill [3]). An upper semi-continuous mapping $f : X \to \mathcal{C}(Y)$ has a non-trivial induced homomorphism in either of the following cases:

(i) X and Y are compact polyhedra such that for all $x \in X$, f(x) is either acyclic or else consists of exactly n acyclic components;

(ii) X is a compact one-dimensional polyhedron with first Betti-number $\leq 1$, and Y is a compact polyhedron.

From this we have theorems 4 and 5 below.

4. (O'Neill [3]). Let X be a compact polyhedron and n a fixed positive integer. Let $f : X \to \mathcal{C}(X)$ be continuous such that, for all $x \in X$, f(x) is either acyclic or else consists of exactly n acyclic components. Then f has a non-trivial homomorphism h such that if $\Lambda(h) \neq 0$, then X has a fixed point under f. Further, if X is acyclic, then there is a fixed point.

Analogous, but weaker results were earlier obtained by Magenes [2] (1950), Darbo [1] (1950) and Dal Saglio [1] (1956).

For n = 1 theorem 2 is the polyhedral form of the theorem of Eilenberg and Montgomery [1] (1946), except that the requirement that f be lower semi-continuous is then superfluous. However, if $n > 1$, upper semi-continuity alone is insufficient. For example, consider the mapping of the interval $[-1,1]$ for which $f(0) = \{-1,1\}$, $f(x) = \{1\}$ for $x < 0$, $f(x) = \{-1\}$ for $x > 0$. Also, if $n > 1$ the space of induced homomorphisms need not be one-dimensional as in the case n = 1.

It does not appear that this result can be generalized by altering the number of components f(x) is permitted to have. For, if S is any finite set of positive integers - except certain sets of the form $\{2,n\}$ and necessarily, $\{1,n\}$ - there is a continuous mapping $f : C^2 \to \mathcal{C}(C^2)$, $C^2$ being the 2-cell, which has no fixed points and which is such that for each point x the number of points in f(x) occurs in S (O'Neill [3]).

5. (O'Neill [3]). Let X be a compact one-dimensional polyhedron with first Betti-number $R_1 \leq 1$. Every continuous mapping $f : X \longrightarrow \mathcal{C}(X)$ has a non-trivial induced homomorphism h such that if $\Lambda(h) \neq 0$, then X has a fixed point under f.

Corollary (Plunkett [1] ). A dendrite has the f.p.p. for continuous closed set-valued mappings.

Ward [7] (1958) obtained the following extension of Plunkett's result which is not included in theorem 5:

6. (Ward [7]). An arcwise connected, heriditarily unicoherent, hereditarily decomposable metric continuum has the f.p.p. for continuous closed set-valued mappings.

The restriction on the Betti-number in theorem 5 cannot be omitted. For let X be a compact one-dimensional polyhedron without end points and such that $R_1 > 1$. If $\varepsilon > 0$ is sufficiently small, the function $f : X \longrightarrow \mathcal{C}(X)$ defined by $f(x) = \{y \in X, \rho(x,y) = \varepsilon\}$ will be continuous if $\rho$ is a suitable metric, and any induced homomorphism of f will be a scalar multiple of the identity homomorphism of H(X). Thus a non-trivial induced homomorphism of such a function would have a non-zero Lefschetz number, contradicting theorem 2.

The condition that the space be one-dimensional is also essential. Strother [1] (1953) showed that no Tychonoff cube with more than one factor has the f.p.p. for continuous closed set-valued mappings. Thus it is necessary to place further conditions on functions defined on spaces of dimension $\geq 2$. In addition to the restrictions stated in O'Neill's theorems (O'Neill [3] ), we have the following possibilities:

7. (Strother [1] ). Let X be a retract of a Tychonoff cube $T = I^A$. Let $f : X \longrightarrow \mathcal{C}(X)$ be continuous such that, for every $x \in X$, f(x) is the product of subsets of I. Then X has a fixed point under f.

8. (Strother [1] ). Let X be a retract of a Tychonoff cube $T = I^A$. Let $\pi_\alpha : X \rightarrow I$ $(\alpha \in A)$ be the natural projection. Let $f : X \longrightarrow \mathcal{C}(X)$ be continuous such that, for some fixed $\beta \in A$ and for all $x \in X$, there is only one point in f(x) which projects onto $\sup \{y_\beta \mid y_\beta \in \pi_\beta [f(x)]\}$. Then X has a fixed point under f.

In each case the proof proceeds by constructing a trace of f, i.e. a continuous function $f' : X \to X$ such that $f'(x) \in f(x)$ for all $x \in X$.

## 1.5. Mappings $f : X \to Y$ such that $X \subset Y$ and $f[X] \not\subset X$

So far we have been concerned with mappings of a space into itself. We now consider a more general situation: If X is a proper subset of a space Y, what conditions must be imposed to ensure the existence of fixed points under a mapping $f : X \to Y$ such that $f[X] \setminus X \neq \emptyset$ ?

As an example, we have the following extension of Brouwer's fixed point theorem for the n-cell:

1. (Knaster, Kuratowski and Mazurkiewicz [1] (1929)). Let $C^n$ be an n-cell in $E^n$, and $f : C^n \to E^n$ continuous such that f maps the boundary of $C^n$ into $C^n$. Then $C^n$ has a fixed point under f.

For two dimensions Sperner [1] (1934) proved the existence of fixed points under slightly weaker assumptions:

2. (Sperner [1] (1934)) . Let $C^2$ be a two-cell in $E^2$ and $f : C^2 \to E^2$ continuous. Then $C^2$ has a fixed point under f if the boundary of $C^2$ contains an arc A such that (i) A contains all the accumulation points of $f[C^2] \setminus C^2$, and (ii) $f[A] \subset C^2$.

Fixed point theorems of the same spirit (and for the two-dimensional case) have been given by Scorza Dragoni [1,2] (1941, 1946), Volpato [1,2] (1946, 1948), Dolcher [1] (1948), and Trevisan [1] (1950).

The Knaster-Kuratowski-Mazurkiewicz theorem was extended to Banach spaces:

3. (Rothe [3] (1938)). If X is a Banach space and f a continuous mapping of the closed unit ball $C = \{x \in X \mid \|x\| \leq 1\}$ into X such that $f[C]$ is compact and the boundary of C is mapped into C, then C has a fixed point under f.

For multi-valued mappings we have the following result:

4. (Eilenberg and Montgomery [1] (1946)). Let $C^n$ be an n-cell in $E^n$, and $\mathcal{C}(E^n)$ the family of non-empty compact subsets of $E^n$. Let $f : C^n \to \mathcal{C}(E^n)$ be an upper semi-continuous mapping which maps the boundary of $C^n$ into $C^n$. If there exists a non-trivial coefficient group with respect to which each f(x) is acyclic (Vietoris

homology), then $C^n$ has a fixed point under f.

It is to be expected that theorems 3 and 4 also hold for locally convex topological linear spaces (with the obvious changes in wording).

It is natural to ask the following question: If $C^n$ and $D^n$ are n-cells such that $C^n$ is <u>properly</u> contained in $D^n$, and f is a continuous mapping of $C^n$ <u>onto</u> $D^n$, does there exist a fixed point under f? For continuous mappings this is in general not true (Hamilton [3] (1948)),but for interior mappings (i.e. continuous, open mappings) we have the following results:

5. (Hamilton [3] (1948)). If f is an <u>interior</u> mapping of a locally connected unicoherent plane continuum M <u>onto</u> a two-cell containing M, then M has a fixed point under f.

Corollary. Let f be an interior mapping of a locally connected plane continuum M, which does not separate the plane, onto a two-cell containing M. Then M has a fixed point under f.

6. (Hamilton [3] (1948)). Let f be an interior mapping of a two-cell C into the plane, such that $C \subset f[C]$. Then C has a fixed point under f.

## 1.6. <u>Spaces with a finite number of holes</u>

Bourgin [3] (1957), using his results on the index of a convexoid space (Bourgin [2] (1955)), proved a number of theorems giving sufficient conditions for the existence of fixed points under continuous mappings of a space with a finite number of holes: His main results are:

1. (Bourgin [3]). Let X be an $AR^*$ (i.e. a space which is homeomorphic to a retract of a Tychonoff cube), and $Y_1, Y_2, \ldots, Y_n$ $(n > 1)$ open subsets of X such that $\bar{Y}_i \cap \bar{Y}_j = \emptyset$ $(i \neq j)$ and such that $\bar{Y}_i$ $(i=1,2,\ldots,n)$ is an $AR^*$. Set $G = \bigcup_{i=1}^{n} Y_i$. Let $f : X \setminus G \to X$ be a continuous mapping such that the boundary of $Y_i$ is mapped into $\bar{Y}_i$ $(i=1,2,\ldots,n)$. Then $X \setminus G$ has a fixed point under f.

This theorem generalizes previous results by Brouwer [5] (1919), Alexander [1] (1922) and Feigl [1] (1928).

2. (Bourgin [3] ). Let E be a reflexive Banach space and $Y_1, Y_2, \ldots, Y_n$ $(n > 1)$ open sets in the weak topology with mutually disjoint closures which are AR*'s. Set $G = \bigcup_{i=1}^{n} Y_i$. Let $f : E \setminus G \to E$ be a continuous mapping which sends the boundary of $Y_i$ into $\bar{Y}_i$ $(i=1,2,\ldots,n)$, and is such that $f^m[E \setminus G]$ is contained in an open ball in E for some integer $m \geq 1$. Then $E \setminus G$ has a fixed point under f.

Göhde [1] (1959) obtained the following partial extension of theorem 2:

3. (Göhde [1] ). Let X be a closed ball in an infinite-dimensional Banach space, and let $Y_i$ $(i=1,2,\ldots,n)$ be mutually disjoint open balls which are contained in X. Set $G = X \setminus \bigcup_{i=1}^{n} Y_i$. Let $f : G \to G$ be continuous such that $f[G]$ is compact. Then G has a fixed point under f.

For results on the existence of fixed points when an annular ring is mapped into itself, the reader is referred to G.D. Birkhoff [1,2] (1913, 1931), Kerékjártó [1,2] (1921, 1923) and Rey Pastor [1] (1945). (Also see p.19.)

## 1.7. Common fixed points

The following theorem is due to Markov [1] (1936) and Kakutani [1] (1938):

1. (Markov [1], Kakutani [1]). Let K be a compact convex subset of a locally convex topological linear space, and let F be a commutative family of continuous affine transformations of K into itself. Then K has a common fixed point under F, i.e. there is an $x \in K$ such that $f(x) = x$ for all $f \in F$.

This theorem was first proved by Markov [1] , who used the Tychonoff fixed point theorem (Tychonoff [1]). Kakutani [1] then sketched a direct proof, and he also outlined a proof of the following theorem:

2. (Kakutani [1]). Let K be a compact convex subset of a locally convex topological linear space and let G be a group of equicontinuous affine transformations of K into itself. Then K has a common fixed point under F.

Despite the similarity in appearance, the theorems are proved along different lines. (For proofs of these theorems, see Dunford and Schwartz [1, p.456-457 ]).

The Markov-Kakutani theorem was extended to a larger class of families of functions by Day [2] (1961). He noted that if $x \in K$ is a fixed point under f, then it is also a fixed point under every iterate of f, i.e. x is fixed under the smallest semigroup of operators on K which includes f. Similarly, x is fixed under every function f of a family F of functions of K into itself, if and only if x is also fixed under every finite product $\underset{i \leq n}{\circ} f_i$ of functions from F. Thus, in the Markov-Kakutani theorem, F may be replaced by $\Sigma(F)$, the smallest semigroup of continuous affine mappings of K into itself which contains F. In this case the commutativity of F is carried to the semigroup $\Sigma(F)$, so the theorem above is equivalent to that obtained by replacing the word "family" by "semigroup". In order to formulate Day's extension of theorem 1, we briefly define a few concepts.

Let $\Sigma$ be a semigroup, and $m(\Sigma)$ the Banach space of all bounded, real-valued mappings x on $\Sigma$, with $\|x\| = \sup\{|x(g)| \mid g \in \Sigma$ . Let e be that element of $m(\Sigma)$ for which $e(g) = 1$ for every $g \in \Sigma$. Let $m(\Sigma)^*$ be the adjoint space of $m(\Sigma)$. A <u>mean</u> on $\Sigma$ is an element $\mu \in m(\Sigma)^*$ such that $\|\mu\| = 1 = \mu(e)$.

The <u>right</u> [<u>left</u>] <u>regular representation of $\Sigma$ over $m(\Sigma)$</u> is the homomorphism [antihomomorphism] defined on $\Sigma$ into the multiplicative semigroup of the algebra of bounded linear mappings of $m(\Sigma)$ into itself by: For each $h \in \Sigma$, $\rho_h$ [$\lambda_h$] is that linear mapping defined by: For each $f \in m(\Sigma)$ and each $g \in \Sigma$

$$(\rho_h f)(g) = f(gh) \quad [(\lambda_h f)(g) = f(hg)] \ .$$

A mean $\mu$ on $\Sigma$ is called <u>right</u> [<u>left</u>] <u>invariant</u> if for each $f \in m(\Sigma)$ and each $h \in \Sigma$

$$\mu(\rho_h f) = \mu(f) \quad [\mu(\lambda_h f) = \mu(f)] \ .$$

A mean is <u>invariant</u> if it is both right and left invariant. $\Sigma$ is called <u>amenable</u> if there exists an invariant mean on $\Sigma$. If we express this in terms of adjoint mappings of the linear mappings $\rho_h$ or $\lambda_h$, a mean is a right, or left, or two-sided, invariant mean if and only if $\mu$ is a fixed point of every $\rho_g^*$, or every $\lambda_g^*$, or both, respectively.

The extended theorem can now be formulated as follows:

3. (Day [2] ). Let K be a compact convex subset of a locally convex topological linear space, and let $\Sigma$ be a semigroup of continuous affine mappings of K into itself. If $\Sigma$ is amenable, or even of it has a left invariant mean, then K has a common fixed point under $\Sigma$ .

Every Abelian semigroup is amenable (Day [1] (1942)), so this theorem is indeed an extension of the Markov-Kakutani theorem. The arguments used in the proof of theorem 3 admits the following generalization:

4. (Day [2] ). Let A(K) be the semigroup of all affine continuous mappings of K into itself, and let A(K) have the topology of pointwise convergence. Let S be any semigroup with a topology in which multiplication is continuous in each variable, and let C(S) be the space of bounded, continuous real-valued functions on S, with the least upper bound norm. If there is a left-invariant mean on C(S), then for each continuous homomorphism $\tau : S \rightarrow A(K)$, K has a common fixed point under $\tau[S]$ .

Since Haar measure defines a left invariant mean on any compact group (see e.g. Halmos [1]), this theorem includes the case where S is a discreet Abelian semigroup or a compact group.

A still unsolved problem concerning the existence of common fixed points was referred to by Isbell [1] (1957): If T is a tree and F is a commutative family of continuous functions $f : T \rightarrow T$, does there exist a common fixed point under F? The answer is in the affirmative provided that the members of F are homeomorphisms (Isbell l.c.), but otherwise little seems to be known, even when T is a compact interval and F contains only two functions. However, it seems that the restriction that F does not contain many functions only adds to the difficulties, for

5. (Myškis [1] (1954). If P is a finite polyhedron with non-vanishing Euler characteristic and F is a one-parameter semigroup of continuous mappings of P into itself, then P has a common fixed point under F.

6. (Hedrlín [1,2] (1961, 1962). Let F be a commutative semigroup of continuous mappings of the closed unit interval $I = [0,1]$ into itself which contains the identity mapping. Suppose that, for some $a \in I$, the orbit $F(a) = \{f(a) \mid f \in F\}$ is a connected set. Then I has a common fixed point under F.

7. (Baayen [1] (1963)); also see Hedrlín [2, p.38] (1962)). Let F be a commutative group of continuous mappings of a topological space X into itself, and let F contain the identity mapping. Let F be maximal as a group, i.e. let F be contained in no other transformation group $G : X \to X$. Then X has a common fixed point under F if and only if F is not a maximal commutative semigroup.

8. (Hedrlín [3] (1962)). Let F be a commutative semigroup of continuous mappings of a topological space X into itself, and let F contain the identity mapping. Then X has a common fixed point under F if and only if the orbit F(a) of some $a \in X$ is a compact space which has the f.p.p. for continuous mappings.

## 1.8. The Lefschetz fixed point formula for non-locally connected continua

We remark here that a quasi-complex (Lefschetz [5, p.323]) need not be locally connected, e.g. Dyer [2] (1956) proved that the finite product of chainable continua (for the latter, see p.66 ) is an acyclic quasi-complex and hence has the f.p.p. for continuous mappings. Also, Wilder [2] (1957) showed that under additional assumptions on the mappings, the Lefschetz fixed point formula can be applied to another class of non-locally connected continua.

A compact Hausdorff space is n-lc at $x \in X$ if, given any neighbourhood U of x, there is a neighbourhood V of x contained in U such that every n-dimensional Čech-cycle on V bounds on U. X is $lc^n$ at x if it is r-lc at x for all $r \leq n$, and it is $lc^\infty$ at x if it is r-lc at x for all r.

If X fails to be $lc^\infty$ at x, then x is an $lc^\infty$-singular point of X. An $lc^\infty$-prime part of X is a component of the closure of the set of all $lc^\infty$-singular points of X.

Wilder [2] proved the following theorems:

1. (Wilder [2] ). Let X be a compact Hausdorff space of finite dimension all of whose Betti numbers are finite and whose $lc^\infty$-prime parts are acyclic (Čech homology with coefficients in a field). If $f : X \to X$ is continuous and maps each $lc^\infty$-prime part into an $lc^\infty$- prime part, and if the Lefschetz number $\Lambda(f) \neq 0$, then there is an $lc^\infty$- prime part of X which is mapped onto itself. In particular, if the $lc^\infty$- prime parts of X have the f.p.p. for continuous mappings, then X has a fixed point under f.

2.(Wilder [2] ). Let X be as in theorem 1. Let f be an upper semi-continuous mapping such that the image of each point $x \in X$ is the union P(x) of a collection of $lc^{\infty}$ - prime parts of X, such that this union is acyclic and such that if x and y are in the same $lc^{\infty}$ - prime part of X, then P(x) = P(y). Let $\Lambda(f)$ be defined as in Begle [2] (also see p.46). Then, if $\Lambda(f) \neq 0$, there is an $x \in X$ such that $x \in f(x)$.

Wilder [2] conjectured that these theorems also hold if the restriction that the mapping sends $lc^{\infty}$ - prime parts into $lc^{\infty}$ - prime parts is dropped, provided that the $lc^{\infty}$ - prime parts are acyclic.

# CHAPTER II

## The Scherrer fixed point theorem and related fixed point theorems

### 2.1. Definitions and introductory remarks

We first define some of the concepts which will be used in this chapter.

A space will be called degenerate if it contains one point only; otherwise, a space will be said to be non-degenerate.

Let X be a connected topological space. A point e of X is an end point of X if, for each neighbourhood U of e, there is a neighbourhood V of e such that $\overline{V} \subset U$ and $\overline{V} \setminus V$ consists of a single point. A point c of X is a cut point of X if $X \setminus \{c\}$ is disconnected. Two points x and y of X are conjugate points (written $x \sim y$) if no point of X separates x and y in X. If $p \in X$ is neither a cut point nor an end point of X, then the set $M(p) = \{x \in X \mid x \sim p\}$ is a simple link of X. A subset of X is an $E_o$-set of X provided that it is maximal with respect to the property of being a connected subset without cut points. X is semi locally connected (s.l.c.) if, for each point $x \in X$ and each neighbourhood U of x, there is a neighbourhood V of x such that $V \subset U$ and $X \setminus V$ has only a finite number of components. If X is s.l.c. then the simple links coincide with the $E_o$-sets. A cyclic element of X is either an end point, a cut point or a simple link of the space. An end element of X is a cyclic element E of X with the property that, if U is a neighbourhood of E, then there is a neighbourhood V of E such that $\overline{V} \subset U$ and $\overline{V} \setminus V$ consists of a single point.

A curve is a one-dimensional continuum.

The reader is referred to Whyburn [1] for information on metric continua and cyclic element theory.

A chain in a topological space is a finite number of open subsets $U_1, U_2, \ldots, U_n$ of the space such that $U_i \cap U_j \neq \emptyset$ if and only if $|i-j| \leq 1$. The sets $U_i$ are called the links of the chain. A chain $\{U_i\}_{i=1}^{n}$ is said to connect two points x and y if $x \in U_1$ and $y \in U_n$. A continuum is chainable if each of its open coverings has a refinement which is a chain. A metric chainable continuum is called snake-like. Each snake-like continuum is imbeddable in the plane (Bing [2] ).

Bing [1] proved that any two non-degenerate hereditarily indecomposable snake-like continua are homeomorphic. Such a continuum is called a pseudo arc.

A circular chain is a finite collection of at least three non-empty open sets $U_1, U_2, \ldots, U_n$ such that $U_1 \cap U_n \neq \emptyset$, and otherwise $U_i \cap U_j \neq \emptyset$ if and only if $|i-j| \leq 1$. A collection G of sets is coherent if, for each proper subcollection H of G, an element of H has a non-empty intersection with an element of $G \setminus H$. A finite coherent collection of open sets is a tree chain if no three of the sets have a point in common and no subcollection is a circular chain. A continuum is tree-like if each of its open coverings has a refinement which is a tree chain. The tree-like continua include among others the trees and certain indecomposable continua. Each plane continuum which does not contain a continuum which separates the plane, is tree-like. (See Bing [2] for information on tree-like continua.)

If X and Y are topological spaces, then a continuous mapping $f : X \rightarrow Y$ is called monotone if $f^{-1}(y)$ is a connected subset of X for every $y \in Y$. f is pseudo-monotone if, whenever A and B are closed connected subsets respectively of X and Y, and $B \subset f[A]$, then some component of $A \cap f^{-1}[B]$ is mapped onto B by f. In general the notion of a pseudo-monotone mapping is independent of the notion of a monotone mapping, but if X is a hereditarily unicoherent continuum, and $f : X \rightarrow Y$ is monotone, then it is pseudo-monotone (Ward [10] ).

The following two unsolved problems play an interesting role in the set-up of this chapter:

(i) Does a plane continuum which does not separate the plane have the f.p.p.?

(ii) Does a tree-like metric continuum have the f.p.p.? (Bing [2] ).

Most of the results to be surveyed in this chapter can be interpreted as partial solutions of one or both of these problems or as generalizations of such partial solutions to either non-metric spaces or multi-valued mappings. This seems to be true even though many of the "partial results" were obtained before either problem was explicitly formulated in the literature. The two problems are in fact different, but the second problem seems to be the more general one, as there exists many tree-like metric continua which are not imbeddable in the plane.

For the sake of clarity, the results for single-valued mappings are grouped together in section 2, even when they were formulated directly for multi-valued mappings in the original publications. The results for multi-valued mappings are surveyed in section 3.

If a mapping of a continuum into itself leaves an end point fixed, the question arises whether there are other fixed points. Results answering questions of this nature are collected in section 4.

## 2.2. Single-valued mappings

One of the main results to be stated in this section is

1. A tree has the f.p.p. for continuous mappings.

The history of this theorem is as follows: In 1926 Scherrer [1] proved that a dendrite has the f.p.p. for continuous mappings. Nöbeling [1] (1932) extended this result to continuous mappings,and another proof was given by Borsuk [3] (1932). It also follows (for a dendrite and continuous mappings) from the following result due to Hopf [2] , in the proof of which he made use of the structures of the nerves of the coverings of the considered space:

2. (Hopf [2] (1937)). If $\alpha$ is a covering of order 2 of a unicoherent locally connected continuum X by closed sets, and $f : X \rightarrow X$ is continuous, then there exists a member $U \in \alpha$ such that $U \cap f[U] \neq \emptyset$.

Wallace [1] (1941) showed that the techniques introduced by Hopf could also be applied to show that a tree has the f.p.p. for continuous mappings, and other proofs of this result were given by Ward [4] (1951) and Capel and Strother [3] (1958), by means of the order-theoretic characterization of trees due to Ward [2] (1954). Ward [4] (1957) also defined a <u>generalized tree</u> in terms of partial order for which he proved a fixed point theorem. Finally, theorem 1 follows from Lefschetz's fixed point formula (Lefschetz [5] (1942)).

Ayres [1] (1930) gave several extensions of Scherrer's theorem to arbitrary Peano continua. His first theorem contains a general result on the cyclic structure of Peano continua:

3. (Ayres [1] (1930)). If X is a Peano continuum and $h : X \to X$ a homeomorphism, then there exists a cyclic element C of X such that $h[C] \subset C$.

From this, three generalizations of Scherrer's theorem follow:

4. (Ayres [1] (1930)). If every cyclic element of a Peano continuum X has the f.p.p. for homeomorphisms, then X has the same property.

5. (Ayres [1] (1930)). If every cyclic element of a Peano continuum X is an n-dimensional simplex (n may vary for different elements), then X has the f.p.p. for homeomorphisms.

6. (Ayres [1] (1930)). If a Peano continuum lies in the plane and does not separate the plane, then it has the f.p.p. for homeomorphisms.

Borsuk [3] (1932) showed that "homeomorphisms" in theorems 4 - 6 may be replaced by "continuous mappings" to give stronger results in the case of theorems 5 and 6.

Kelley [1] (1939) extended theorem 3 to non-locally connected metric continua:

7.(Kelley [1] (1939)). If X is a metric continuum and $h : X \to X$ a homeomorphism, then there exists a subcontinuum Y of X such that $h[Y] = Y$ and Y has no cut points.

From this follows

8. (Kelley [1] (1939). If X is a metric continuum and $h : X \to X$ a homeomorphism, then there exists either a fixed point in X or else an $E_0$-set Y such that $h[Y] \subset Y$.

9. (Kelley [1] (1939)). If every $E_0$-set in a metric continuum X has the f.p.p. for homeomorphisms, so also has X.

If X is semi locally connected, then the $E_0$-sets and the cyclic elements coincide, and thus theorems 8 and 9 imply theorems 3 and 4 respectively.

In 1940 Kelley [2] obtained related results for continuous mappings.

10. (Kelley [2] (1940)). If f is a continuous mapping of a metric continuum X into itself, then there exists a continuum Y which is a subset of a simple link of X such that $f[Y] \supset Y$. If Y is degenerate, then there is a fixed point: Hence, if $f : X \to X$ is continuous, then there exists either a fixed point in X or else a simple link C such that $C \cap f[C]$ is a non-degenerate continuum.

11. (Kelley [2] (1940)). If f is a continuous mapping of a metric continuum X into itself, then there exists a compact subset A of a simple link of X such that $f[A] = A$.

12.(Kelley [2] (1940)). If f is a continuous mapping of a metric continuum X into itself which carries each simple link into a simple link (e.g. if the inverse of no point separates a simple link in X), then there exists a simple link C of X such that $f[C] \subset C$.

For Peano continua, theorem 12 implies theorem 3, and the fixed point theorem for dendrites follows from theorem 10. Ward [3,10] (1956, 1962) showed that theorem 7 holds for arbitrary continua and for monotone and pseudo-monotone mappings.

Hamilton [1] (1938) extended theorem 6 to a class of non-locally connected metric continua and proved theorems related to theorems 3 - 5 for this class of continua.

13. (Hamilton [1] (1938)). If X is a decomposable non-degenerate metric continuum and $h : X \rightarrow X$ a homeomorphism, then there exists a <u>proper</u> subcontinuum Y of X such that $Y \cap f[Y] \neq \emptyset$.

14. (Hamilton [1] (1938)). If X is a decomposable and hereditarily unicoherent non-degenerate metric continuum and $h : X \rightarrow X$ a homeomorphism, then there exists a <u>proper</u> subcontinuum Y of X such that $h[Y] \subset Y$.

15. (Hamilton [1] (1938)). A hereditarily decomposable and hereditarily unicoherent metric continuum has the f.p.p. for homeomorphisms.

Theorem 15 admits as application in the plane:

16. (Hamilton [1] (1938)). A hereditarily decomposable plane continuum which does not separate the plane and which contains no domain, has the f.p.p. for homeomorphisms.

17. (Hamilton [1] (1938)). If D is a bounded, simply connected plane domain whose closure does not separate the plane and whose boundary is hereditarily decomposable, then $\overline{D}$ has the f.p.p. for homeomorphisms.

It is unknown whether a plane continuum which does not separate the plane has the f.p.p., even for homeomorphisms. Choquet [1] (1941) showed that if C is any plane continuum which does not separate the plane and $h : C \rightarrow C$ is a homeomorphism which is extensible to a homeomorphism of the plane onto itself and if h is periodic with period $\neq 2$, then C has a fixed point under h. Cartwright and

Littlewood [1] (1951) proved that a plane acyclic continuum has the f.p.p. for homeomorphisms which are extensible to homeomorphisms of the plane onto itself.

Theorem 15 was extended to hereditarily decomposable and unicoherent (non-metric) continua and monotone and pseudo-monotone mappings (Ward [10] (1962)). In particular, a continuum each of whose non-degenerate subcontinua has a cut point, has a fixed point under a pseudo-monotone mapping.

Borsuk [7] (1954) partially extended theorem 15 to continuous mappings:

18. (Borsuk [7] (1954)). An arcwise connected, hereditarily unicoherent metric continuum has the f.p.p. for continuous mappings. In particular, an arcwise connected, hereditarily acyclic curve has the f.p.p. for continuous mappings.

Borsuk l.c. proved that an arcwise connected, hereditarily unicoherent continuum is hereditarily decomposable. Thus, for homeomorphisms his result is included in Hamilton's theorem (theorem 15 above). Theorem 18 was extended to non-metric continua by Young [2] (1960).

A corollary of theorem 18 is that a contractible curve has the f.p.p. for continuous mappings. Kinoshita [2] (1953), however, gave a counter-example to the widely held conjecture that every contractible continuum must have the f.p.p. for continuous mappings. The join of the space in his example with a point is a cone which lacks the f.p.p.

We now consider generalizations of the fixed point theorem for trees to non-compact, non-locally connected spaces. Young [1] (1946) defined a <u>generalized dendrite</u> as a locally connected Hausdorff space X such that if $x,y \in X$ and $L_1$ and $L_2$ are two chains of connected subsets from x to y, then some member of $L_1$ intersects some member of $L_2$ outside $\{x,y\}$. If X is compact, this is equivalent with X being a tree. Young proved that every two distinct points x and y of a generalized dendrite X are the non-cut points of a unique compact, connected and locally connected set P such that each point of $P \setminus \{x,y\}$ separates x and y in X, and he called such a set P a "pseudo arc". To avoid confusion with the term <u>pseudo arc</u> as defined on p.67, we shall use the term <u>generalized arc</u> instead of "pseudo arc". Young l.c. obtained the following generalizations of the fixed point theorem for trees:

19. (Young [1] (1946)). If X is an arcwise connected generalized dendrite such that the union of any monotone increasing sequence of generalized arcs of X is contained in a generalized arc, then X has the f.p.p. for continuous mappings. Conversely, if X is an arcwise connected generalized dendrite which has the f.p.p. for continuous mappings, then the union of any monotone increasing sequence of generalized arcs of X is contained in a generalized arc.

By the introduction of local connectivity by a change of topology, Young used theorem 18 to deduce

20. (Young [1] (1946)). If X is an arcwise connected Hausdorff space such that the union of any monotone increasing sequence of arcs is contained in an arc, then X has the f.p.p. for continuous mappings.

Ward [8] (1959) obtained a result that includes the abovementioned theorems of Borsuk and Young (theorems 18, 19 (first part) and 20). A <u>topological chain</u> is a continuum which has exactly two end points. A topological space is said to be <u>topologically chained</u> if, for every two distinct points $x,y \in X$, there is a topological chain in X which contains both x and y. Let X be a topologically chained space in which the topological chains are unique, i.e. every two distinct points $x,y \in X$ are the end points of precisely one topological chain, denoted by $[x,y]$. A <u>ray with end point</u> e of X is the union of a maximal nest of chains which have e as common <u>end point.</u> If R is a ray with end point e and $x \in X$, let

$$A(R,x) = R \setminus [e,x] \cup \{x\}, \quad K_R = \cap \{A(R,x) \mid x \in X\}.$$

Consider the condition

(Fe) If R is a ray with end point e, then $K_R$ has the f.p.p. for continuous mappings.

We now state Ward's results.

21. (Ward [8] (1959)). If X is an arcwise connected Hausdorff space in which the union of any nest of arcs is contained in an arc, then the arcs in X are unique and X satisfies (Fx) for each $x \in X$.

22. (Ward [8] (1959)). An arcwise connected, hereditarily unicoherent continuum satisfies (Fx) for each $x \in X$.

23. (Ward [8] (1959)). Let X be a topologically chained space with unique chains and suppose there exists a point $e \in X$ such that (Fe) is satisfied. Then X has the f.p.p. for continuous mappings.

From theorems 21 and 22 it follows that the class of continua for which theorems 18, 19 and 20 hold, is contained in the class for which theorem 23 holds.

Hamilton [4] (1951) introduced a new technique by making explicit use of the fact that a chainable continuum has arbitrarily fine open coverings, each of whose (finite collection of) elements are totally ordered, to present an elegant proof of

24. (Hamilton [4] (1951)). A chainable continuum has the f.p.p. for continuous mappings.

Actually Hamilton proved the theorem for snake-like continua only, but a slight modification of his arguments yields a proof of theorem 24.

Dyer [2] (1956) obtained the following extension of Hamilton's result:

25. (Dyer [2] (1956)). The topological product of an arbitrary family of chainable continua has the f.p.p. for continuous mappings.

Theorem 24 was generalized in another direction also. A snake-like continuum is, by definition, the inverse limit of a system of arcs, and it is not hard to prove that if a space is the inverse limit of a system of arcs, then it is a chainable continuum, as was observed by Rosen [1] (1959). However, it is unknown whether a chainable continuum is the inverse limit of a system of arcs. Rosen established the following partial extension of theorem 24:

26. (Rosen [1] (1959)). Let X and Y be the inverse limits of systems of arcs over directed sets A and A' respectively (definitions as in Eilenberg and Steenrod [1] ), and let $\varphi : A \to A'$ be an isomorphism, i.e. $\varphi$ is one-to-one-, $\alpha \leq \beta$ in A implies $\varphi(\alpha) \leq \varphi(\beta)$ in A' and $\varphi[A]$ is cofinal in A'. Let $f, g : X \to Y$ be continuous mappings of which g is onto. Then X has a coincidence point under f and g, i.e. there exists a point $x_0 \in X$ such that $f(x_0) = g(x_0)$.

Theorem 26 was in turn partially extended (and properly extended in the special case where Y = X and $g : X \to X$ is the identity mapping):

27. (Mioduszewski and Rochowski [1] (1962)). Let $\{X_\alpha, \pi_{\alpha\beta}, A\}$ be an inverse system of compact polyhedra $\{X_\alpha\}_{\alpha \in A}$ over a directed set A, where the projections $\pi_{\alpha\beta} : X_\beta \to X_\alpha$ $(\alpha \leq \beta)$ are continuous and onto, and such that, for every continuous mapping f of $X_\beta$ onto $X_\alpha$, there is a point $x_\beta \in X_\beta$ such that $f(x_\beta) = \pi_{\alpha\beta}(x_\beta)$.

Then the inverse limit of the system $\{X_\alpha, \Pi_{\alpha\beta}, A\}$ has the f.p.p. for continuous mappings.

Both theorem 26 and theorem 27 imply the fixed point theorem for snake-like continua. Theorem 27 also has the following interesting corollary:

28. (Mioduszweski and Rochowski [1] (1962)). Let $\{X_\alpha, \Pi_{\alpha\beta}, A\}$ be an inverse system of compact polyhedra such that $X_\alpha \subset X_\beta$ for all $\alpha, \beta \in A$ with $\alpha \leq \beta$. Let $\{\Pi_{\alpha\beta}\}_{\alpha,\beta\in A}$ be retractions, i.e. $\Pi_{\alpha\beta}|X_\alpha$ is the identity mapping on $X_\alpha$, and let each $X_\alpha$ ($\alpha \in A$) have the f.p.p. for continuous mappings. Then the inverse limit of $\{X_\alpha, \Pi_{\alpha\beta}, A\}$ has the f.p.p. for continuous mappings.

Mioduszweski and Rochowski [1] stated the following problem which includes the question whether a tree-like continuum has the f.p.p.: If all the $X_\alpha$ in the inverse system $\{X_\alpha, \Pi_{\alpha\beta}, A\}$ have the f.p.p. for continuous mappings, and the $\Pi_{\alpha\beta}$ are onto, does the inverse limit of the system have the f.p.p.?

## 2.3. Multi-valued mappings

Wallace showed that the techniques introduced by Hopf [2](see theorem 2 of section 2) could be applied to extend the fixed point theorem for trees to a certain class of multi-valued mappings.

1. (Wallace [1] (1941)). A tree has the f.p.p. for upper semi-continuous continuum-valued mappings.

Capel and Strother [3] (1958) used order-theoretic methods to give another proof of theorem 1. Theorem 1 also follows from Begle's extension of the Lefschetz fixed point theorem (Begle [1] (1950); see section 3 of Chapter I).

Attention has already been drawn to the fact that, to ensure the existence of fixed points under arbitrary closed set-valued mappings, it is necessary to impose upper semi-continuity and lower semi-continuity on the mappings (O'Neill [3] (1957); see section 4 of Chapter I). Furthermore, the spaces which have the f.p.p. for continuous closed set-valued mappings constitute a fairly small subclass of those which have the f.p.p. for (single-valued) continuous mappings. For example:

2. (Plunkett [1] (1956)). (a) A dendrite has the f.p.p. for continuous closed set-valued mappings.

(b) Conversely, if a Peano continuum has the f.p.p. for continuous closed set-valued mappings, then it is a dendrite.

Theorem 2(a) was extended to non-metric continua:

3. (Ward [7] (1958)). A topologically chained [1], hereditarily unicoherent and hereditarily decomposable continuum has the f.p.p. for continuous closed set-valued mappings. In particular, since an arcwise connected, hereditarily unicoherent continuum contains no indecomposable continuum (e.g. Borsuk [7,p.17]), such a space has the f.p.p. for continuous closed set-valued mappings.

The arcwise connected metric continua which have the f.p.p. for upper semi-continuous continuum-valued mappings are characterized by hereditary unicoherence:

4. (Ward [9] (1961)). An arcwise connected metric continuum has the f.p.p. for upper semi-continuous continuum-valued mappings if and only if it is hereditarily unicoherent.

Thus, for Peano continua the class of spaces which have the f.p.p. for continuous closed set-valued mappings coincides with the class of spaces possessing the f.p.p. for upper semi-continuous continuum-valued mappings.

We now turn our attention to snake-like continua. Ward [6] (1958) showed that Hamilton's argument in the case of single-valued mappings (Hamilton [4] (1951)) can also be applied to continuous set-valued mappings. In fact it can be extended to chainable continua, as was observed by Rosen [1] (1959).

5. (Ward [6] (1958), Rosen [1] (1959)). A chainable continuum has the f.p.p. for continuous closed set-valued mappings.

Rosen l.c. established results which in the metric case are generalizations of theorem 5 both with respect to the class of mappings and the class of spaces.

6. (Rosen [1] (1959)). Let X and Y be the inverse limit of systems of arcs over directed sets A and A' respectively (definitions as in Eilenberg and Steenrod [1] ). Let $\varphi : A \longrightarrow A'$ be an isomorphism, i.e. $\varphi$ is one-to-one, $\alpha \leq \beta$ in A implies $\varphi(\alpha) \leq \varphi(\beta)$ in A' and $\varphi[A]$ is cofinal in A'. Let $\mathcal{S}(Y)$ denote the family of nonempty closed subsets of Y, and let $f,g : X \longrightarrow \mathcal{S}(Y)$ be upper semi-continuous mappings such that g is onto and the graphs of f and g are connected subsets of $X \times Y$. Then X has a coincidence point under

---

1) See p. 72 for the definition.

f and g, i.e. there exists a point $x_0 \in X$ such that $f(x_0) \cap g(x_0) \neq \emptyset$.

Corollary. Let X be a snake-like continuum and $f : X \longrightarrow \mathcal{S}(X)$ an upper semi-continuous mapping such that the graph of f is connected. Then X has a fixed point under f.

7. (Rosen [1] (1959)). Let X and Y be as in theorem 6. Let $\mathcal{C}(Y)$ denote the family of non-empty subcontinua of Y, and let f,g : $X \longrightarrow \mathcal{C}(Y)$ be upper semi-continuous mappings of which g is onto. Then X has a coincidence point under f and g.

Corollary. A snake-like continuum has the f.p.p. for upper semi-continuous continuum-valued mappings.

8. (Rosen [1] (1959)). Let X and Y be as in theorem 6. Let $f : X \longrightarrow \mathcal{S}(Y)$ be continuous, and $g : X \longrightarrow \mathcal{S}(Y)$ upper semi-continuous, onto and such that the graph of g is connected. Then X has a coincidence point under f and g.

Theorem 8 implies theorem 5 in the case of snake-like continua.

2.4. Fixed end points

There are a few isolated results in the literature of fixed point theory which state sufficient conditions for the existence of more than one fixed point when the existence of at least one is known.

1. (Schweigert [1] (1944), Wallace [2] (1945), Ward [1,3] (1954, 1956)). Let X be a continuum, and E an end element containing no cut points of X. Let f be a monotone mapping of X onto itself such that f[E] = E. Then $X \setminus E$ contains a non-empty subcontinuum without cut points.

Corollary. If X is a tree and $E = \{ e \}$, e being an end point of X, then there exists a fixed point of f distinct from e.

2. (Young [1] (1946)). Let X be a generalized dendrite 1) such that the union of any monotone increasing sequence of generalized arcs 1) is contained in a generalized arc. Let h be a homeomorphism of X onto itself, and e a point of X which is fixed under h and which is an end point of every generalized arc containing it. Then there exists a point $x_0 \neq e$ which is fixed under f.

In particular, the conclusion of the theorem holds if "generalized dendrite" is replaced by "arcwise connected Hausdorff space" and "generalized arc" by "arc".

Results analogous to the Markov-Kakutani theorem (see section

1) See p.71 for the definitions.

7 of Chapter I) was obtained by Wallace [3] (1949) and Wang [1] (1952). Wallace l.c. considered a continuum X and a group Z which is required to be a topological space (but not necessarily a topological group). Let a continuous function $f : Z \times X \longrightarrow X$ be given which satisfies:

(i) $f(e,x) = x$, for all $x \in X$, where e is the unit element of Z;

(ii) $f(z,f(z',x)) = f(zz',x)$, for all $x \in X$ and all $z,z' \in Z$.

For each $z \in Z$, set $z(x) = f(z,x)$, for all $x \in X$. Then Z can be considered ("somewhat incorrectly") as a group of homeomorphisms acting on X.

A subset A of X is called <u>Z-invariant</u> provided that $z[A] = A$ for all $z \in Z$. Wallace proved

3. (Wallace [3] (1949)).

(a) If Z is Abelian, then there is a non-empty Z-invariant subcontinuum of X which has no cut points. Moreover, there exists a non-empty Z-invariant cyclic element in X.

(b) If Z is Abelian and no proper subcontinuum of X is Z-invariant, then X has no cut points.

(c) If Z is connected and metric, then every end point and every non-degenerate cyclic element of X is Z-invariant.

Wallace l.c. raised the following question: If X is a Peano continuum and G is a compact transformation group of X such that an end point of X is G-invariant, do there exist other G-invariant points of X? Wang [1] (1952) solved the problem for spaces much more general than Peano continua by proving the following theorem:

4. (Wang [1] (1952)). Let G be a transformation group of an arcwise connected Hausdorff space X, and let e be a G-invariant end point of X. Then there is no other G-invariant point of X if and only if, for each neighbourhood U of e, the set $G[U] = \bigcup \{ g[U] \mid g \in G \}$ coincides with X. If G is also compact, then there exists a G-invariant point of X distinct from e.

# CHAPTER III

## Miscellany

### 3.1. Partially ordered sets and spaces

#### 3.1.1. Ordered sets

A relation $\leq$ on a set P is a quasi-order on P if it is reflexive and transitive. If it is also anti-symmetric on P, i.e. if $x \leq y$ and $y \leq x$ can never occur simultaneously, then $\leq$ is a partial order on P. If for every $x, y \in P$ we have either $x \leq y$ or $y \leq x$, then $\leq$ is a total (also, linear) order on P. We write $x < y$ if $x \leq y$ and $x \neq y$. A mapping $f : P \to P$ is isotone provided $f(x) \leq f(y)$ for all $x, y \in P$ such that $x \leq y$.

The fixed point theorems of Abian and Brown [1] (1961)(henceforth referred to as AB [1]) for partially ordered sets include most of the previously known results as well as the more or less simultaneously published results of Pelczar [1] (1961). Their proofs are based entirely on the definitions of partially and well-ordered sets, and except in the case of theorem 4 and corollary 4 below, make no use of any form of the axiom of choice.

Let P be a set, partially ordered by $\leq$ . Let $f : P \to P$ be a mapping. For each $a \in P$, an a-chain $C_r$ is a subset of P satisfying the following conditions (AB [1]):

(1) $C_r$ is well ordered, with a as its first and r as its last element;

(2) if $z \in C_r$ and $z \neq r$, then $f(z) \in C_r$, $z < f(z)$, and there exists no $y \in C_r$ for which $z < y < f(z)$;

(3) if T is a non-empty subset of $C_r$, then sup T exists and is an element of $C_r$.

Let $W(a) = \{r \in P \mid \exists \text{ an a-chain } C_r \text{ having r as its last element}\}$.

From (2) it follows that $W(a) = \{a\}$ except when $a < f(a)$. The set W(a) has the following properties (AB [1]):

(i) If $r \in W(a)$ and $C_r$ is an a-chain with last element r, then $C_r \subset W(a)$.

(ii) If $r \in W(a)$ and $r < f(r)$, then $f(r) \in W(a)$.

(iii) If $r, s \in W(a)$ and $C_r$ is an a-chain with last element r, then either $s \in C_r$ or $r < s$.

(iv) If $r \in W(a)$, there is just one a-chain $C_r$ with last element r, namely $\{x \in W(a) \mid x \leq r\}$.

Thus, for given P, f and a, $C_r$ is uniquely determined by r.

We now state the main results of AB [1].

1. (AB [1]). Let P be a partially ordered set, f a mapping of P into itself, and a an arbitrary element of P. Then

(4) W(a) is well ordered with a as first element.

Moreover, if $c = \sup W(a)$ exists, then

(5) W(a) is an a-chain with c its last element, and

(6) $c \nless f(c)$.

2. (AB [1] ; also see Pelczar [1] ). Let P be a partially ordered set in which

(7) if W is a non-empty well ordered subset of P, then sup W exists.

Let $f : P \to P$ be an isotone mapping such that

(8) there exists an element $a \in P$ such that $a \leq f(a)$.

Then there exists at least one element $c \in P$ such that $c = f(c)$. In fact, $c = \sup W(a)$ is such an element.

Corollary 1. (AB [1] , Knaster [1] (1928), Tarski [1] (1955); also see G. Birkhoff [1, p.54] ). Let $f : P \to P$ be an isotone mapping of a complete lattice into itself. Then $x_0 = f(x_0)$ for some $x_0 \in P$.

Corollary 2. (AB [1] ; also see Pelczar [1] ). Let P be a partially ordered set in which

(9) every non-empty well ordered subset W of P which is bounded above has a sup.

Let $f : P \to P$ be isotone and let there exist two elements $a, b \in P$ such that

(10) $a \leq f(a) \leq f(b) \leq b$.

Then there exists $c \in P$ such that $f(c) = c$ and $a \leq c \leq b$. In fact, $c = \sup W(a)$ is such an element.

Corollary 3. (AB [1], G.Birkhoff [1, p.54, example 4] ). If f is an isotone mapping of a conditionally complete lattice into itself and if there exist two elements $a, b \in P$ such that $a \leq f(a) \leq f(b) \leq b$, then $f(c) = c$ for some $c \in P$ with $a \leq c \leq b$.

3. (AB [1], G. Birkhoff [1, p.44, example 4]). Let P be a partially ordered set in which
(11) sup of every non-empty well ordered subset W of P exists.
Let $f : P \to P$ be a mapping such that
(12) $x \leq f(x)$, for all $x \in P$.

Then there exists at least one element $c \in P$ such that $c = f(c)$. In fact, for each $a \in P$, $c = \sup W(a)$ is such an element.

4. (AB [1]). Let P be a partially ordered set in which
(13) each non-empty well ordered subset $W \subset P$ which is bounded above has a sup.
Let $g : P \to P$ be a mapping such that
(14) if $g(x) < g(y)$, then $x < y$ for every two elements $x, y \in P$, and
(15) for $x, y, s \in P$, if $g(x) \leq s \leq g(y)$, then $g^{-1}(s) \neq \emptyset$.
Let $f : P \to P$ be isotone, and let there exist $a, b \in P$, with $a < b$, satisfying

$$g(a) \leq f(a) \text{ and } f(b) \leq g(b).$$

Then there exists at least one element $c \in P$ such that $a \leq c \leq b$ and $f(c) = g(c)$.

Corollary 4. (AB [1]). If in theorem 4 instead of (14) we assume that g is isotone, then the conclusion of theorem 4 remains valid provided P is linearly ordered.

The results of Pelczar [1] actually are slightly weaker than those of AB [1], e.g. instead of (7) it is assumed that the sup of every non-empty subset of P exists.

The following generalized form of corollary 1 above was proved by Tarski [1] (1955):

5. (Tarski [1]). Let L be a complete lattice and F a commutative family of isotone mappings of L into itself. Let Q be the set of all common fixed points of L under F, i.e.
$Q = \{x \in L \mid f(x) = x \text{ for all } f \in F\}$. Then Q is a non-empty complete lattice.

Davis [1] (1955) showed that the property of having the f.p.p. for isotone mappings is also sufficient for a lattice to be complete. Thus

6. (Davis [1]). A lattice is complete if and only if it has the f.p.p. for continuous mappings.

Wolk [1] (1957) obtained an analogous characterization for a class of partially ordered sets which includes the lattices. Let P be a partially ordered set with a greatest and a least element. A subset S of P is up-directed [down-directed] if each pair of elements of S has an upper bound [a lower bound] in S. P is Dedekind complete if each up-directed subset of P has a sup in P and each down-directed has an inf in P.

For $A \subset P$, let

$$A^{*} = \{x \in P \mid a \leq x \text{ for all } a \in A\}, \text{ and}$$

$$A^{+} = \{x \in P \mid x \leq a \text{ for all } a \in A\}.$$

P is uniform if $A^{*}$ is a down-directed set for every up-directed subset A, and if $B^{+}$ is an up-directed set for every down-directed subset B. An isotone mapping $f : P \to P$ is directable if $\{x \in P \mid x \leq f(x)\}$ is an up-directed subset of P.

It is easy to verify that a complete lattice is a Dedekind complete, uniform, partially ordered set with a least and a greatest element, and that every isotone mapping of a lattice into itself is directable. Thus the following theorems of Wolk [1] include the theorems of Tarski [1] (for the special case when F in theorem 5 above consists of a single mapping) and Davis [1] :

7. (Wolk [1] ). If P is a partially ordered set such that each up-directed subset of P has a sup in P, then P has the f.p.p. for directable functions.

8. (Wolk [1] ). If P is a uniform partially ordered set which has the f.p.p. for directable functions, then P is Dedekind complete.

Hence we have

9. (Wolk [1] ). A uniform partially ordered set is Dedekind complete if and only if it has the f.p.p. for directable functions.

Theorem 7 is a direct consequence of theorem 2 (Abian and Brown [1] ).

Ward [5] (1957) obtained a necessary and sufficient condition for a class of partially ordered sets, which includes the lattices, to be compact (in the interval topology) in terms of the f.p.p. for isotone mappings. A partially ordered set P is a semi-lattice if each pair of elements of P has an inf in P. A semi-lattice is complete if each non-empty subset of P has an inf in P. Ward's results are

10. (Ward [5] ). Let P be a semi-lattice and $f : P \longrightarrow P$ isotone. If P is compact in the interval topology, then the set Q of fixed points of P under f is non-empty. If P is a complete semi-lattice, and $Q \neq \emptyset$, then Q is a complete semi-lattice.

11. (Ward [5] ). A semi-lattice P is compact in the interval topology if and only if P has the f.p.p. for isotone functions.

3.1.2. Ordered spaces

Let X be a topological space endowed with a quasi order $\leq$. The quasi order is lower [upper] semi-continuous if, whenever $a \nleq b$ [$b \nleq a$] in X, there is a neighbourhood U of a such that if $x \in U$, then $x \nleq b$ [$b \nleq x$]. The quasi order is semi-continuous if it is both upper and lower semi-continuous. It is continuous if, whenever $a \nleq b$ in X, there are neighbourhoods U and V of a and b respectively, such that if $x \in U$ and $y \in V$ then $x \nleq y$. A quasi ordered topological space (QOTS) is a topological space together with a semi-continuous quasi order. If the quasi order is a partial order, then the space is a partially ordered topological space (POTS).

For $x \in X$, let $L(x) = \{a \in X \mid a \leq x\}$, $M(x) = \{a \in X \mid x \leq a\}$, $E(x) = L(x) \cap M(x)$.

Clearly, the statement that X is a QOTS is equivalent to the assertion that L(x) and M(x) are closed sets, for each $x \in X$.

A chain of a quasi-ordered set X is a subset of X which is totally ordered by the quasi order. A maximal chain is a chain which is properly contained in no other chain.

For information on ordered topological spaces, see Ward [1] and the papers quoted there.

In 1945 Wallace [2] proved the following fixed point theorem, which he applied to obtain an extension of the Schweigert theorem (Schweigert [1] ):

1. (Wallace [2] ). Let X be a compact Hausdorff QOTS, satisfying:

(i) there exists a unique element $e \in X$ such that $e \leq x$ for all $x \in X$;

(ii) each set L(x) is totally ordered;

(iii) for every two elements $x$ and $y$ distinct from $e$, there exists an element $z \in X$ such that $z \leq x$ and $z \leq y$.

If $f$ is a homeomorphism of $X$ onto itself such that both $f$ and $f^{-1}$ is isotone, then there exists an element $x_0 \neq e$ in $X$ such that both $x_0 \leq f(x_0)$ and $f(x_0) \leq x_0$.

If $\leq$ is a partial order on $X$, then $x_0$ is a fixed point distinct from $e$.

Ward [1] (1954) continued along these lines and used the results to obtain fixed point theorems for continuous mappings of hereditarily unicoherent continua (Ward [1,4,7,9,10] ), already referred to in Chapter II. We now state Ward's results:

2. (Ward [1] ). Let $X$ be a Hausdorff QOTS with compact maximal chains and let $f : X \to X$ be continuous and isotone. A necessary and sufficient condition that there exist a non-empty compact set $K \subset E(x_0)$ for some $x_0 \in X$, is that there exist $x \in X$ such that $x$ and $f(x)$ are comparable, i.e. such that either $x \leq f(x)$ or $f(x) \leq x$.

Corollary 1. If $X$ is partially ordered, then a necessary and sufficient condition that $f$ has a fixed point is that there exist $x \in X$ such that $x$ and $f(x)$ are comparable.

If $X$ is a partially ordered set with an element $e \in X$ such that $e \leq x$ for all $x \in X$, and $A$ is a subset of $X$, we say that $A$ is <u>bounded away</u> from $e$ provided there is $y \in X \setminus E(e)$ such that $A \subset M(y)$.

3. (Ward [1] ). Let $X$ be a Hausdorff QOTS with compact maximal chains and suppose there exist $e \in X$ such that $e \leq x$ for all $x \in X$. Let $f : X \to X$ be a continuous and isotone mapping which also satisfies:

(i) there exists $x \in X \setminus E(e)$ such that $x$ and $f(x)$ are comparable;

(ii) if $x$ satisfies (i), then either the sequence $\{f^n(x)\}_{n=1}^{\infty}$ is bounded away from $e$, or there exists $y \in X$ such that $x \in E(f(y))$ and $f(y) \leq y$.

Then there is an $x_0 \in X \setminus E(e)$ and a non-empty compact set $K \subset E(x_0)$ such that $f[K] = K$.

Corollary 2. If $X$ is partially ordered, then there is a fixed point under $f$ distinct from $e$.

Corollary 3. Let $X$ and $f$ be as in theorem 2, and suppose $X$ satisfies the equivalent conditions

(i) there exists $u \in X$ such that $L(u) = X$,

(ii) for $x,y \in X$, there exists $z \in X$ such that $x \leq z$ and $y \leq z$.

Then there is a non-empty compact set $K \subset E(x_0)$, for some $x_0 \in X$, such that $f[K] = K$.

Corollary 4. Let X and f be as in corollary 3, and let X be partially ordered. Then X has a fixed point under f.

Corollary 5. Let X be a compact Hausdorff QOTS satisfying (i) and (ii) of corollary 3, as well as

(iii) there exists $e \in X$ such that $e \leq x$ for all $x \in X$, and $E(e) \neq X$.

Let $f : X \longrightarrow X$ be continuous, isotone and onto. Then there is a non-empty compact set $K \subset E(x_0)$, for some $x_0 \in X \setminus E(e)$, such that $f[K] = K$.

Corollary 6. Let X and f be as in corollary 5. If X is partially ordered, then there exists a fixed point distinct from e.

In concluding this section we remark that the "long line" has the f.p.p. for continuous mappings, as follows from a more general result by Young [1] (1946).

3.2. The product of spaces

If X and Y are topological spaces, each of which has the f.p.p. for continuous mappings, does their topological product also have this property? (Strother [1] (1953)). In general, this is not true (Connell [1] (1959), Klee [5] (1960); also see section 5 of this chapter). However, Cohen [1] (1956) showed that the answer is in the affirmative if X and Y are totally ordered sets which are compact in the interval topology. Since a compact, totally ordered space has the f.p.p. for continuous mappings if and only if it is connected, Cohen's result may be stated as follows:

1. (Cohen [1] ). If X and Y are compact connected totally ordered spaces, then their topological product has the f.p.p. for continuous mappings.

Since a compact connected and totally ordered Hausdorff space is a chainable continuum (see p.66 for the latter), the above result is a special case of the following simultaneously published result of Dyer [2] (1956):

2. (Dyer [2] ). The topological product of an arbitrary family of chainable continua has the f.p.p. for continuous mappings.

To prove theorem 2, Dyer first showed that the product of a finite family of chainable continua has the f.p.p. for continuous mappings. Theorem 2 then follows from this result and the following simple but useful fact:

3. (Dyer [2]). Let $\mathcal{A}$ be a family of compact Hausdorff spaces. Then the topological product of the elements of $\mathcal{A}$ has the f.p.p. for continuous mappings if and only if the topological product of each finite subfamily of $\mathcal{A}$ has the f.p.p. for continuous mappings.

Theorem 1 is related to a result of Ginsburg [1] (1954), who proved that if X and Y are totally ordered sets, each of which has the f.p.p. for similarity transformations (i.e. one-to-one transformations onto), then also both the direct sum and the Cartesian product $X \times Y$ (ordered lexicographically) have the f.p.p. for similarity transformations.

### 3.3. Hyperspaces

Let X be a continuum, and $\mathcal{S}(X)$ [$\mathcal{C}(X)$] the space consisting of the non-empty closed [non-empty closed and connected] subsets of X, with the finite topology.

1. (Kelley [3] (1942)). For any metric continuum X, $\mathcal{C}(X)$ is an AR if (and only if) X is locally connected. Hence, if X is a locally connected metric continuum, then $\mathcal{C}(X)$ has the f.p.p. for continuous mappings.

2. (Capel and Strother [1] (1956), Hammond Smith [1] (1961)). If X is an ANR*, then both $\mathcal{S}(X)$ and $\mathcal{C}(X)$ have the f.p.p. for continuous mappings.

3. (Segal [1] (1962)). If X is a snake-like continuum, then $\mathcal{C}(X)$ is an acyclic quasi-complex in the sense of Lefschetz [5, p.323] and hence has the f.p.p. for continuous mappings.

PROBLEM (Segal [1] ). For what class of continua is $\mathcal{C}(X)$ a quasi-complex (Lefschetz [5] ) or a semi-complex (Browder [5])?

### 3.4. Non-continuous mappings

Nash [1] (1956) defined a connectivity mapping of a space X into a space Y as a mapping $f : X \to Y$ such that, if A is a connected subset of X, then $f|A$ is a connected subset of $X \times Y$; equivalently, $f : X \to Y$ is a connectivity mapping if and only if the induced mapping $f^*: X \to X \times Y$, defined by $f^*(x) = (x, f(x))$ for all $x \in X$, transforms connected subsets of X onto connected subsets of $X \times Y$. Obviously, a continuous mapping $f : X \to Y$ is a connectivity mapping. On the other hand, there are connectivity mappings of the n-cell into itself, for each $n \geq 2$, which are not continuous (Hamilton [5] (1957)). Nash [1] inquired whether the n-cell has the f.p.p. for connectivity mappings. Hamilton l.c. answered this question affirmatively [1], by introducing the concept of a peripherally continuous mapping. A mapping $f : X \longrightarrow Y$ is said to be <u>peripherally continuous</u> if, for each $x \in X$ and for each neighbourhood V of x and each neighbourhood U of f(x), there exists a neighbourhood W of x which is contained in V and such that f maps the boundary of W into U. Hamilton [5] showed:

1. (Hamilton [5] ). A connectivity mapping of the n-cell into itself, $n \geq 2$, is peripherally continuous.[2]

2. (Hamilton [5] ). The n-cell, $n \geq 2$, has the f.p.p. for peripherally continuous mappings.

It is easy to see that the one-cell has the f.p.p. for connectivity mappings. Hence we have:

3. (Hamilton [5] ). The n-cell has the f.p.p. for connectivity mappings.

It is not known whether a peripherally continuous mapping of the n-cell into itself, $n \geq 2$, is necessarily a connectivity mapping. The following is an example of a peripherally continuous mapping of the one-cell $I = [0,1]$ into itself which is not a connectivity mapping and which has no fixed point: for x rational, let $f(x) = \frac{\pi}{4}$, and for x irrational, let $f(x) = \frac{3}{4}$. (Hamilton [5] ).

Hamilton l.c. also gave an example of a mapping g of the n-cell $C^n$ into itself, for any $n \geq 1$, such that

(i) g carries connected subsets of $C^n$ onto connected subsets of $C^n$;

(ii) $g^*$ sends connected and locally connected subsets of $C^n$ onto connected subsets of $C^n \times C^n$;

(iii) g is not a connectivity mapping;

(iv) g is not peripherally continuous;

(v) $C^n$ has no fixed point under g.

Stallings [1] (1959) observed an error in Hamilton's proof of theorem 1. He remedied this defect and introduced other types of non-continuous transformations for which he proved fixed point theorems. We now state these definitions and theorems.

---------------

[1],[2] As was noted by Stallings [1], Hamilton's proof of theorem 1 contains an error. However, Stallings l.c. showed that the theorem is true.

A function $f : X \to Y$ is a <u>local connectivity mapping</u> if there exists an open covering $\{U_\alpha\}_{\alpha \in A}$ of X such that, for each $\alpha \in A$, $f|U_\alpha$ is a connectivity mapping of $U_\alpha$ into Y.

A <u>polyhedron</u> P is understood to be a finite simplicial complex K together with a geometrical realization $|K|$. A <u>subpolyhedron</u> Q of P is a subcomplex L of K, together with the geometrical realization $|L|$ which is identified with a subset of $|K|$ in a canonical way. The <u>Cartesian product</u> $P \times Q$ of the polyhedra $P = (K, |K|)$ and $Q = (L, |L|)$ is given by the product $K \times L$ of their respective complexes (as defined in Eilenberg and Steenrod [1,p.67]), and a geometrical realization $|K \times L|$ which is identified in a canonical way with $|K| \times |L|$, so that the projections $|K \times L| \to |K|$, $|K \times L| \to |L|$ are induced by simplicial mappings $K \times L \to K$, $K \times L \to L$; and so that the diagonal $\Delta$ of $|K| \times |K|$ is the geometrical realization of a simplicial complex D which is isomorphic to K, and $(D, \Delta)$ is a subpolyhedron of $P \times P$.

For convenience, the polyhedron $P = (K, |K|)$, the simplicial complex K and the geometrical realization $|K|$ will henceforth be considered as one and the same.

If P is a polyhedron, then a subset N of P is a <u>polyhedral open set</u> if $P \setminus N$ is a subpolyhedron of P.

Let P and Q be polyhedra. A function $f : P \to Q$ is <u>polyhedrally almost continuous</u> if, for each polyhedral open subset N of $P \times Q$ such that $f \subset N$, there exists a continuous function $g : P \to Q$ such that $g \subset N$.

Let X and Y be topological spaces. A function $f : X \to Y$ is <u>almost continuous</u> if, for each subset N of $X \times Y$ such that $f \subset N$, there exists a function $g : X \to Y$ such that $g \subset N$.

A polyhedron P is <u>locally peripherally connected</u> if, for each $p \in P$ and each neighbourhood U of p, there exists a neighbourhood V of p, such that $V \subset U$ and the boundary of V is connected.

Let $C^{k+1}$ denote the closed unit ball in $E^{k+1}$, and let $S^k$ be its bounding k-sphere. A metric space $(X, \rho)$ is <u>uniformly locally n-connected</u> if, for each $\varepsilon > 0$, there exists a $\delta > 0$ such that, for each $x \in X$ and each integer k, $0 \le k \le n$, and each continuous function $f : S^k \to U_\delta(x) = \{y \in X \mid \rho(x,y) < \delta\}$, there is an extension of f to a continuous mapping $f^* : C^{k+1} \to U_\varepsilon(x)$.

Stallings [1] proved the following theorems:

4. (Stallings [1] ). Let P be a polyhedron, N a polyhedral open set in $P \times P$. If P has a fixed point under every continuous mapping $g : P \to P$ for which $g \subset N$, then P has a fixed point under every polyhedrally almost continuous mapping $f : P \to P$ for which $f \subset N$.

5. (Stallings [1] ). Let X be a Hausdorff space and N an open subset of $X \times X$. If X has a fixed point under every continuous mapping $g : X \to X$ for which $g \subset N$, then X has a fixed point under every almost continuous mapping $f : X \to X$ for which $f \subset N$.

6. (Stallings [1] ). If $f : P \to Y$ is a local connectivity mapping of a locally peripherally connected polyhedron P into a regular Hausdorff space Y, then f is peripherally continuous.

This is a generalization of Hamilton's theorem 1.

7. (Stallings [1] ). Let P be a locally peripherally connected polyhedron of dimension n and X a uniformly locally (n-1)-connected metric space. Let $f : P \to X$ be peripherally continuous. Then f is almost continuous.

Corollary 1. If P is a polyhedron of simplicial dimension n which is of Menger-Urysohn dimension $\geq 2$, and $f : P \to X$ is a connectivity mapping, where X is uniformly locally (n-1)-connected, then f is almost continuous.

Corollary 2. If P and Q are polyhedra and $f : P \to Q$ is a connectivity mapping, then f is polyhedrally almost continuous.

Combining corollary 1 and theorem 5, we have:

8. (Stallings [1] ). Let P be a polyhedron of Menger-Urysohn dimension $\geq 2$, and N an open subset of $P \times P$. If P has a fixed point under every continuous mapping $g : P \to P$ for which $g \subset N$, then P has a fixed point under every connectivity mapping $f : P \to P$ for which $f \subset N$.

Combination of corollary 2 and theorem 4 gives:

9. (Stallings [1] ). Let P be an arbitrary polyhedron and N a polyhedral open subset of $P \times P$. If P has a fixed point under every continuous mapping $g : P \to P$ for which $g \subset N$, then P has a fixed point under every connectivity mapping $f : P \to P$ for which $f \subset N$.

For the set N occurring in some of the above theorems we may of course take the product space $X \times X$ (or $P \times P$).

### 3.5. Compactness and fixed points

In this section we shall consider single-valued mappings only, and we shall say that a space X has the f.p.p. if it has a fixed point under every continuous mapping $f : X \to X$.

The question whether there exists a relation between compactness and the f.p.p. was considered by Klee [2] (1955) and Connell [1] (1959). Although for most fixed point theorems the compactness of the space is assumed, in general compactness and the f.p.p. are only vaguely related. For example, there exists a Hausdorff space which has no compact subsets except finite sets, and yet it has the f.p.p. (Connell [1] ). De Groot [1] (1959) obtained the result that there exists a family $\mathcal{S}$ of $2^{\underline{c}}$ topologically distinct subsets of the Euclidean plane (c denotes the potency of the real number system), each of which has potency c, is connected and locally connected, contains no compact subsets except countable ones and has the f.p.p. These sets are rigid, i.e. if $X \in \mathcal{S}$ and $f : X \to X$ is continuous, then either f is a constant mapping or the identity mapping.

However, in some cases it is possible to stipulate a necessary and sufficient condition for the f.p.p. to hold in terms of compactness. Thus Tychonoff [1] (1935) proved that a compact convex subset of a locally convex topological linear space has the f.p.p., and Klee [2] obtained the following partial converse of Tychonoff's theorem:

1. (Klee [2] ). If X is a locally convex metric topological linear space and K is a non-compact convex subset of X, then K lacks the f.p.p.

It is unknown whether Tychonoff's theorem or theorem 1 holds in an arbitrary topological linear space.

By a topological ray is meant a homeomorphic image of the half-open interval [0,1] with the usual topology. The following fact follows easily from a slight extension of the Tietze mapping theorem:

2. (Klee [2] ). If S is a normal space which contains a topological ray as a closed subset, then there is a fixed point free null-homotopic mapping of S into S.

Klee [2] applied this result to show that certain spaces lack the f.p.p. We recall the following definitions in order to formulate these results: A subset B of a topological linear space X is bounded if, for each neighbourhood U of the zero element of X, there is a number t such that $B \subset tU$. A set is linearly bounded if its intersection with each line is bounded. A topological linear space is locally [linearly] bounded if it contains a non-empty [linearly] bounded open subset.

3. (Klee [2]). Let X be a topological linear space and H a convex subset of X. Then if at least one of the following statements is true, H must contain a topological ray as a closed subset:

(i) X is locally convex and H is unbounded;

(ii) X is metric and H is not complete in the natural uniformity;

(iii) X is isomorphic to a subspace of a product of locally linearly bounded topological linear spaces, and some bounded subset of H fails to be precompact (for the latter, see Kelley [4,p.198]);

(iv) H is closed, locally compact and unbounded;

(v) X is locally convex and metric, and H is non-compact;

(vi) X is locally bounded and H is non-compact.

Combining 2, 3 (v) and Tychonoff's theorem, we have:

4. (Klee [2]). For a convex subset H of a locally convex metric topological linear space, the following conditions are equivalent:

(i) H is compact;

(ii) H has the f.p.p.;

(iii) no closed subset of H is a topological ray.

Theorem 4 and its proof are analogous to work of Dugundji [1] (1951). He showed that if C and S are respectively the unit cell and the unit sphere of an infinite-dimensional normed linear space, then C can be retracted onto S, whence C must lack the f.p.p. Kakutani [4] (1943) and Klee [1] (1953) showed that in a large class of infinite-dimensional normed linear spaces, the unit cell actually admits a homeomorphism onto itself without fixed points. In fact, for any infinite dimensional normed linear space X there exists a homeomorphism of period two without fixed points of X onto X which maps C onto C. (Klee [4] (1956)). From a result of Klee [2,theorem 5.8, p.44] it follows that every convex subset H of a normed linear space such that H is non-compact, closed, locally compact, and at least two-dimensional, admits a homeomorphism onto itself without fixed points. On the other hand, since the unit cell of a reflexive Banach space X is compact in the weak topology of X, it has the f.p.p. for weakly continuous mappings.

Klee also established the following results:

5. (Klee [2] ). Let X be a non-compact, connected, locally connected, locally compact metric space. Then X contains a topological ray as a closed subset.

If X is a space which has the f.p.p., then X is connected, and every retract of X also has the f.p.p. Hence

6. (Klee [2] ). If X is a non-compact, locally connected, locally compact metric space, then X lacks the f.p.p.

From 2, 5 and known properties of ANR's (Lefschetz [6] ), we have

7. (Klee [2] ). Let X be a locally compact, connected metric absolute neighbourhood retract. Then X is compact if and only if every null-homotopic mapping of X into X has at least one fixed point.

Connell [1] defined a chain of arcs as a countable set of arcs $\{A_n\}_{n=1}^{\infty} = \{[b_n, c_n]\}_{n=1}^{\infty}$ such that $c_n = b_{n+1}$ for all n. The following result of Connell is a consequence of theorem 5:

8. (Connell [1] ). If X is a metric space with the f.p.p.,then every locally finite chain of arcs is finite.

For, if $\{A_n\}$ is a locally finite infinite chain of arcs in X, then their union $A = \bigcup_{n=1}^{\infty} A_n$ is a non-compact,connected, locally connected, locally compact metric space. Hence A must contain a topological ray T as a closed subset, by 5, and since A is closed in X, T is closed in X. Hence X cannot have the f.p.p., according to 2.

We recall here the following fixed point theorem of Young [1] (1946) for (not necessarily compact) arcwise connected spaces:

9. (Young [1] ). If X is an arcwise connected Hausdorff space in which the union of every monotone increasing sequence of arcs is contained in an arc, then X has the f.p.p.

Young [2] (1960) used this result to obtain the following necessary condition for a space not to have the f.p.p.:

10. (Young [2] ). Let M be an arcwise connected continuum which lacks the f.p.p. Then M contains either

(i) a continuum $N_1$ for which there is a continuous mapping $f : N_1 \longrightarrow S^1$ (the one-sphere in $E^2$) which is onto and such that no closed proper subset of $N_1$ is mapped onto $S^1$ by f, and which is such that at most one point of $S^1$ has a non-degenerate inverse, that inverse being connected; or

(ii) a continuum $N_2$ which contains a subset R which is the one-to-one continuous image of a half-open interval and which is dense in $N_2$, but which has no interior relative to $N_2$; or

(iii) a continuum $N_3$ which is the union of a set R which is the continuous one-to-one image of a half-open interval, and a continuum B, and for which there is a continuous mapping $f : N_3 \to K$, K being the union of the circles $x^2 + y^2 = \frac{2}{n} y$, $n = 1,2,3,\ldots$, such that f is one-to-one on $N_3 \setminus B$, such that $f[B] = \{(0,0)\}$, and such that no closed proper subset of $N_3$ is mapped onto K by f.

Examples.

(a) Connell [1]. This is an example of a Hausdorff space which contains no compact subsets except finite sets and yet has the f.p.p. Let $X = [0,1]$ and let $\mathcal{U}$ be the collection of all subsets S of X such that there exists a set A, open in the usual topology of X, and a countable (infinite or finite) set B so that $S = A \setminus B$. Then $(X, \mathcal{U})$ is a topological space with the abovementioned properties.

That $(X, \mathcal{U})$ has the f.p.p. follows from the following fact (Connell [1]):

Let X be a set and $\mathcal{V}$ a topology for X such that $(X, \mathcal{V})$ is a regular space with the f.p.p. Let $\mathcal{U}$ be a stronger topology for X (i.e. $A \in \mathcal{V}$ implies $A \in \mathcal{U}$) such that if $R \in \mathcal{U}$, then the closure of R is the same in both spaces. Then $(X, \mathcal{U})$ has the f.p.p.

(b) Connell [1]. This is an example of a non-compact metric space U which has the f.p.p. and yet $U \times U$ lacks the f.p.p. U is locally compact at all but one point. Let $f(x) = \sin \pi/(1-x)$ for $0 \leq x < 1$, $f(1) = 1$. Let $U = \{(x, f(x)) \mid 0 \leq x \leq 1\}$ and let U have the relative topology as a subset of the plane.

It is easy to see that U has the f.p.p. To show that $U \times U$ lacks the f.p.p., Connell constructed an infinite, locally finite chain of arcs in $U \times U$ (see theorem 8 of this section).

(c) Connell [1]. This is an example of a non-compact, separable, locally contractible metric space V which has the f.p.p. Let $I_0 = \{(x,y) \in E^2 \mid 0 \leq x \leq 1,\ y = 0\}$, and for each integer $n \geq 1$, let $I_n = \{(x,y) \in E^2 \mid x = \frac{1}{n},\ 0 \leq y \leq 1\}$. Let $V = \bigcup_{n=0}^{\infty} I_n$. It is not difficult to prove that V has the f.p.p., and it also follows at once from theorem 9 above.

(d) Connell [1]. This is an example of a non-compact plane set W which has the f.p.p., while the closure of W lacks the f.p.p.

Let A be the square (not including its interior) with (0,-2), (4,-2), (4,2) and (0,2) as its four corners. Let A' = $= A \setminus \{(0,y) \mid -1 < y < 1\}$, $B = \{(x,y) \quad 0 \leq x \leq 1, \; y = \sin \frac{1}{x}\}$ and $W = A' \cup B$. W has the f.p.p. Now, $\overline{W} = A \cup B$, and if B is projected onto $\{(0,y) \mid -1 < y < 1\}$, and A is rotated through 90 degrees, then we have a continuous mapping of $\overline{W}$ into itself without fixed points.

(e) Klee [2] (1955), [5] (1960). Klee constructed a non-compact plane set X which combines the properties of the spaces in the examples (b) - (d) of Connell [1] (1959). In addition, X is an absolute retract which is locally compact at all but one point. (Compare theorem 6).

Let $l^2$ be the Hilbert space consisting of all sequences $x = (x^1, x^2, \ldots)$ of real numbers $x^i$ such that $\sum_{i=1}^{\infty} |x^i|^2 < \infty$. Let Y be the set of all points $y = (y^1, y^2, \ldots)$ of $l^2$ such that $y^i \neq 0$ for at most one i and always $0 \leq y^i \leq 1$. If $\vartheta$ is the origin (0,0,...) of $l^2$ and $\delta_n$ is the point of $l^2$ such that $\delta_n^n = 1$ and $\delta_n^i = 0$ for $i \neq n$, then Y is the union of the segments $\sigma_n = [\vartheta, \delta_n]$ having the common end point $\vartheta$. Obviously Y is contractible and locally contractible. Further, Y has the f.p.p. (The latter follows, e.g. from theorem 9 above.))

In the product space $l^2 \times l^2$, let P be the infinite polygon whose vertices, in order, are as follows: $(\vartheta, \delta_1)$, $(\delta_1, \vartheta)$, $(\vartheta, \delta_2)$, $(\delta_2, \vartheta), \ldots, (\vartheta, \delta_n)$, $(\delta_n, \vartheta), \ldots$ . It is easy to verify that P is a closed subset of $Y \times Y$, P a topological ray. Hence $Y \times Y$ lacks the f.p.p., according to theorem 2 of this section.

It remains only to describe a bounded plane homeomorph X of Y such that $\overline{X}$ lacks the f.p.p. For each $t \in [0, \pi]$ and each positive integer n, let $x_n(t) = (1 + \frac{t}{n}) \cos t$ and $y_n(t) = (-1)^n (1 + \frac{t}{n}) \sin t$. Let $\tau_n$ denote the arc consisting of all points $(x_n(t), y_n(t))$ for $t \in [0, \pi]$. Then each arc $\tau_n$ has (1,0) as an end point and $X = \bigcup_{n=1}^{\infty} \tau_n$ is homeomorphic with Y. But $\overline{X}$ contains the unit circle S and admits a retraction onto S. Hence $\overline{X}$ does not have the f.p.p.

(f) Boland [1]. This example shows that "locally compact" in theorem 6 cannot be replaced by "peripherally compact". (A topological space is <u>peripherally compact</u> if each of its points has arbitrarily small neighbourhoods with compact boundaries.)

For each integer $n \geq 1$, let $K_n$ be the subset of $E^3$ consisting of all points $(x,y,z)$ such that

$$\text{either} \quad \begin{cases} x = \frac{1}{n}, \\ 0 \leq y \leq 1, \\ z = 0, \end{cases} \qquad \text{or} \quad \begin{cases} y = \frac{2p+1}{2^n} \quad (0 \leq p \leq 2^{n-1}), \\ (x - \frac{1}{2n})^2 + z^2 = \frac{1}{4n^2}, \\ z \geq 0 \quad . \end{cases}$$

Let $K_0 = \{(x,y,z) \in E^3 \mid 0 \leq x \leq 1,\ y=0,\ z=0\}$,

$$A = \bigcup_{n=0}^{\infty} K_n .$$

Then A is a non-locally compact, peripherally compact and locally connected space which has the f.p.p. The latter follows,e.g., from theorem 9 above.

### 3.6. Fixed point classes and essential fixed points

Two fixed points $x_1$ and $x_2$ of a topological space X under a continuous mapping $f : X \to X$ are said to be in the same fixed point class (with respect to f) if there exists a path P from $x_1$ to $x_2$ such that P is homotopic to $f[P]$ with the end points fixed. (Nielsen [1] (1927)). Nielsen's theory of fixed point classes for the orientable closed surfaces of genus $\geq 2$, the elementary parts of which is summarized below, was generalized to the finite polytopes by Wecken [1] (1939), using the Leray-Schauder theory of the fixed point index for these spaces (Leray-Schauder [1]). Browder [5] (1960), resorting to the theory of the fixed point index as extended by himself (see section 2 of hapter I), observed that these results may be extended to Hausdorff spaces which are compact, connected, locally pathwise connected and semi-locally simply connected, the latter meaning that each sufficiently small Jordan curve is contractible. Then each fixed point class is open in X, and since the set S(f) of fixed points of X under f is compact, there are only finitely many fixed point classes, and each component of S(f) is contained in a fixed point class. Each fixed point class corresponds to the fixed points of X which are covered by the fixed points of $\tilde{X}$, the universal covering space of X, under one of the mappings $\tilde{f}$ which covers f. Since each fixed point class is open in S(f), an index can be assigned to it, and the classes with a fixed non-zero index are deformed into one another under homotopies of f.

The "stability" of a fixed point was studied by Fort [1] (1950), Kinoshita [1] (1952), O'Neill [1] (1953) and Browder [4] (1960). Let X be a Hausdorff space and let $X^X$ denote the space of continuous mappings $f : X \to X$, with the compact-open topology. Let $p \in X$ be a fixed point under $f \in X^X$. Then p is an <u>essential fixed point</u> if, for each neighbourhood U of p, there exists a neighbourhood V of f such that U has a fixed point under $g|U$ for all $g \in V$ (Fort [1] ). Then, e.g., the closed unit interval has no essential fixed points under the identity mapping. Fort l.c. showed that if $f \in X^X$, $p \in X$ and p has arbitrarily small neighbourhoods V such that V has the f.p.p. and $f[\bar{V}] \subset V$, then p is an essential fixed point under f.

The notion of an essential fixed point was generalized by Kinoshita [1] and O'Neill [1] : A <u>component</u> C of the fixed point set S(f) is <u>essential</u> if all mappings g close to f in the compact-open topology have fixed points in a prescribed neighbourhood of C. Kinoshita showed that every continuous null-homotopic mapping f of an ANR into itself has an essential fixed point. O'Neill extended this result by showing the essentiality of any component of the fixed point set of a mapping with non-zero index.

Browder [4] considered the following stronger question: Let X be a Hausdorff space, U an open subset of $X \times I$ (I denotes the closed unit interval $[0,1]$ ), F a continuous mapping of $\bar{U}$ into X. Let $\pi$ be the natural projection of $X \times I$ into X, $\psi_t$ the partial inverse of $\pi$ defined by $\psi_t(x) = (x,t)$ for all $x \in X$. If $f_o = F\,\psi_o$, $f_1 = F\,\psi_1$, and we are given a component C of the fixed point set $S(f_o)$ of the mapping $f_o$ of $\psi_o^{-1}[U]$ into X, does there exist a connected set $C_1$ in $X \times I$ which contains $C \times \{0\}$, intersects $X \times \{1\}$, and is composed of points $(x,t) \in C_1$ for which $F(x,t) = x$?

Let $U_t = \psi_t^{-1}[U]$, $f_t = F\,\psi_t : \bar{U}_t \to X$. The above question essentially asks for a connected set of fixed points of $\bar{U}_t$ under $f_t$, $0 \le t \le 1$, which contains the given component C of fixed points under $f_o$. It is the natural generalization of the question of the existence of a continuous function $\phi : I \to X$ such that $\phi(t) \in \bar{U}_t$ for all $t \in I$, and $f_t(\phi(t)) = \phi(t)$, with $\phi(0) \in C$. There are trivial counter examples to the existence of such functions $\phi$, for instance small deformations of the identity mapping of an even dimensional sphere.

Browder [4] used the theory of the fixed point index to establish the following theorems, which encompasses the results of Kinoshita [1] and O'Neill [1] :

1. (Browder [4] ). Let X be a Hausdorff space, U an open subset of $X \times I$, F a continuous mapping of $\overline{U}$ into a compact Hausdorff space Y lying in a category A for which a fixed point index is defined. (Thus Y may be an ANR$^*$, a neighbourhood retract of a convexoid space, or an HLC$^*$ space.) Let G be a continuous mapping of $Y \times I$ into X, H the mapping of $\overline{U}$ into X given by $H(x,t) = G(F(x,t),t)$. Let $\psi_t$ be the natural injection of X into $X \times I$, $\psi_t(x) = (x,t)$, $U_t = \psi_t^{-1}[U]$, $h_t = H\psi_t$ mapping $\overline{U}_t$ into X. Suppose that $h_t$ has no fixed points on the boundary of $U_t$ for $t \in I$. Let $U' = G^{-1}[U]$, $U_o' = \psi_o^{-1}[U']$, $f_o = F\psi_o$, $g_o = G\psi_o$. Suppose that $i(f_o g_o, U_o') \neq 0$. (In the case in which X itself lies in A, we may make the simpler assumption that $i(h_o, U_o) \neq 0$.)

Then there exists a connected set $C_1$ in U intersecting both $X \times \{0\}$ and $X \times \{1\}$ such that $h_t(x) = x$ for all $(x,t) \in C_1$.

Corollary. Let X be an ANR$^*$, O an open subset of X, f a continuous mapping of $\overline{O}$ into X having no fixed points on the boundary of O. Then if $i(f,O) \neq 0$, f has an essential component of fixed points in O.

2. (Browder [4] ). Let X be a locally convex topological linear space, U an open subset of $X \times I$, F a continuous mapping of $\overline{U}$ into a compact convex subset K of X. Suppose that $f_t = F\psi_t$ has no fixed points on the boundary of $U_t = \psi_t^{-1}[U]$ for $t \in I$, and $i(f_o, U_o) \neq 0$. Then there exists a compact connected set $C_1$ in U intersecting both $X \times \{0\}$ and $X \times \{1\}$ such that $f_t(x) = x$ for all $(x,t) \in C_1$.

3. (Browder [4] ). Let X be a Hausdorff space, U an open subset of $X \times I$, F a continuous mapping of $\overline{U}$ into a compact space lying in a category A on which a fixed point index is defined, G a continuous mapping of $Y \times I$ into X. Let H be the continuous mapping of $\overline{U}$ into X given by $H(x,t) = G(F(x,t),t)$, $(x,t) \in \overline{U}$. Let $U_t = \psi_t^{-1}[U]$, $h_t = H\psi_t$. Suppose that $h_t$ has no fixed points on the boundary of $U_t$, for all $t \in I$. Let C be a component of the fixed point set of $h_o$ and suppose that the following condition is satisfied:

If $U' = G^{-1}[U]$, $U_o' = \psi^{-1}[U']$ and $g_o = G\psi_o$, $f_o = F\psi_o$, the mapping $f_o g_o$ is defined on $U_o'$, which is an open subset of Y. Let $C' = g_o^{-1}[C]$. Then there exists a neighbourhood V of C' in Y such that for any open subset $V_1$ contained in V and containing C' for which $f_o g_o$ has no fixed points on the boundary of $V_1$, we have $i(f_o g_o, V_1) \neq 0$.

Then there exists a compact connected set $C_1$ in U which contains $C \times \{0\}$, is composed of points $(x,t)$ for which $h_t(x) = x$, and intersects $(X \times \{1\}) \cup (X \times \{0\} \setminus C \times \{0\})$.

The condition of theorem 3 is expressed briefly by saying that C has a non-null index with respect to $h_o$. Theorem 3 then becomes the statement that each component of the fixed point set of $h_o$ with non-null index is contained in a component of S, the set of $(x,t) \in U$ for which $H(x,t) = x$, which intersects $X \times \{1\}$.

A particular case in which the condition of theorem 3 is satisfied is that in which C is a single point $x_o$ with non-null index with respect to $h_o$.

3.7. Contractive mappings

The following well-known theorem is due to Banach [1] (1932): Let $(X,\rho)$ be a complete metric space, and $f : X \rightarrow X$ a continuous mapping for which there exists a number k, $0 < k < 1$, such that $\rho(f(x),f(y)) < k\,\rho(x,y)$ for all $x,y \in X$. Then X has a unique fixed point under f.

This theorem was extended in various ways, and has wide applications in analysis. An expository account together with a large number of applications may be found in the paper of Nemyčkiĭ [1] (1936) and in chapter 2 of Miranda [1] (1949). For more recent results the reader is referred to Deleanu [1] (1957), Luxemburg [1] (1958), Albrecht and Karrer [1] (1960), Monna [1] (1961) and Edelstein [1,2] (1961, 1962).

Brodskiĭ and Milman [1] (1948) obtained fixed point theorems for non-expansive and non-contractive mappings of a compact metric space with normal structure into itself. (See Dunford and Schwartz [1, p.459] for a summary of their results.)

3.8. Mappings of spheres into Euclidean spaces

The following theorems have been the starting-point of extensive investigations on the existence of coincidence points under mappings of spheres into Euclidean spaces:

1. (Borsuk [4] (1933)). If $f : S^n \rightarrow E^n$ is continuous, then there is a pair of antipodal points $x, -x \in S^n$ such that $f(x) = f(-x)$.

2. (Lusternik-Schnirelmann [1] (1930), Borsuk [4] (1933)). For every covering of $S^n$ by n+1 closed sets, there is at least one member of the covering which contains a pair of antipodal points.

3. (Kakutani [3] (1942)). Let $f : S^2 \to E^1$ be continuous. Then there exist three orthogonal points $a_0, a_1, a_2 \in S^2$ such that $f(a_0) = f(a_1) = f(a_2)$.

The reader is referred to Yang [1,2] (1954, 1955) for far-reaching generalizations of these theorems and a complete bibliography of their development. Theorem 1 was also extended to multi-valued mappings of $S^n$ into $E^n$ (Jaworowski [1] (1956), and to Banach spaces in the case of single-valued mappings (Krasnoselskiĭ [2] (1950), Altman [1] (1958) and Granas [2] (1962)).

### 3.9. Periodic mappings

If Y is the set of all fixed points of a metric space X under a periodic mapping of X into itself, what topological properties of Y can be deduced from those of X? Considerable work in answering this question has been done since 1934 by Smith (see e.g. Smith [1]). The spaces most thoroughly studied have been the Euclidean spaces and spheres. The motivating question is to determine to what extent does a periodic homeomorphism of $E^n$ or of $S^n$ resemble an orthogonal transformation. In particular, is it equivalent to an orthogonal transformation? Smith showed that for many homology properties and prime periods, the conjecture is correct. Thus, if Y is the fixed point set of a periodic homeomorphism of $E^n$ $[S^n]$, then Y is in some sense homologically similar to $E^r$ $[S^r]$ for some $r \leq n$. The reader is referred to Smith [1,2], Floyd [1,2,3], Swan [1] and Borel et al. [1] for further information.

In striking contrast with the results for Euclidean spaces is Klee's result (Klee [3] (1956)) which states that if Y is a compact [closed] subset of an infinite - dimensional Hilbert space X, then X admits a periodic homeomorphism whose fixed point set is Y [is homeomorphic to Y].

### 3.10. Almost fixed points

There are several theorems to the effect that if f is a mapping of a space X into itself, then there is at least one point $x_0 \in X$ which in some sense is near to its image $f(x_0)$. Usually either X is non-compact and lacks the f.p.p., or f is non-continuous, and in the compact case the property that there exists a point which is "near" to its image is equivalent to the f.p.p.

The first three theorems below are examples of the first mentioned possibility.

1. (Hopf [2] (1937)). Let X be a unicoherent topological space and $\alpha$ a covering of order two of X by closed connected sets. Let $f : X \to X$ be continuous. Then there exists a member U of $\alpha$ such that $U \cap f[U] \neq \emptyset$, or equivalently: there exists a point $x_0 \in X$ such that $x_0$ and $f(x_0)$ lie in the same member of $\alpha$.

2. (Fort [2] (1954)). Let G be a bounded open subset of the Euclidean plane $E^2$ which is homeomorphic to the open unit disk $D = \{x \in E^2 \mid \|x\| < 1\}$ and whose boundary is locally connected. Let $f : G \to G$ be continuous. Then for each $\varepsilon > 0$ there exists a point $x = x(\varepsilon) \in G$ such that $\|x-f(x)\| < \varepsilon$.

Inspection shows that Fort's proof is equally valid for the following assertion:

3. (Fort [2] ). Let d be a positive number and let $B^n = \{x \in E^n \mid \|x\| < d\}$. Let $f : B^n \to B^n$ be continuous. Then for each $\varepsilon > 0$ there exists a point $x \in B^n$ such that $\|x-f(x)\| < \varepsilon$.

Klee's results (Klee [8] (1961)) fall under the second category. They extend the fixed point theorems for continuous mappings of compact convex subsets of locally convex topological linear spaces, described in Chapter I, to "nearly continuous" mappings of such spaces.

For $\varepsilon > 0$, a mapping f of a topological space X into a metric space $(M,\rho)$ is called <u>$\varepsilon$-continuous</u> if each point $x \in X$ has a neighbourhood U such that $\operatorname{diam} f[U] \leq \varepsilon$. For $\delta \geq 0$, a <u>$\delta$-fixed point</u> under a mapping $f : M \to M$ is a point $x \in M$ such that $\rho(x,f(x)) \leq \delta$; f is called a <u>$\delta$-mapping</u> if each point of M is $\delta$-fixed under f. (Klee [8] (1961)).

Klee obtained the following results:

4. (Klee [8]). Let P be a compact convex polyhedron in a Euclidean space, and $f : P \to P$ $\varepsilon$-continuous. Then there exists a continuous mapping $g : P \to P$ such that $\|g(p)-f(p)\| \leq \varepsilon$ for all $p \in P$. Consequently some point of P is $\varepsilon$-fixed under f.

5. (Klee [8] ). Let C be a compact convex subset of a normed linear space, $f : C \to C$ $\varepsilon$-continuous, and $\varepsilon' > \varepsilon$. Then some point of C is $\varepsilon'$-fixed under f.

A metric space M is said to have the <u>proximate fixed point property</u> (p.f.p.p.) if, for each $\varepsilon > 0$ there exists $\tau_\varepsilon > 0$ such that M has an $\varepsilon$-fixed point under each $\tau_\varepsilon$-continuous mapping of M into itself.

6. (Klee [8] ). If a metric space M has the p.f.p.p., then so has every compact retract of M.

7. (Klee [8] ). If a compact metric space has the p.f.p.p., then so has every metric homeomorph of M.

Since an AR is a retract of the Hilbert cube, it follows from 5 - 7 that

8. (Klee [8] ). Every AR has the p.f.p.p.

A compact metric space which has the p.f.p.p. evidently also has the f.p.p. for continuous mappings. The converse need not be true: Klee [8] gave an example of a plane continuum which has the f.p.p. for continuous mappings, but lacks the p.f.p.p. Klee [10] asked whether a Peano continuum which has the f.p.p. for continuous mappings must necessarily have the p.f.p.p.

Generalization of the above results 4 - 8 to uniform spaces are almost immediate. Theorem 4 is easily extended to "nearly upper semi-continuous" mappings of P into the family of non-empty closed convex subsets of P. The resulting generalization of Kakutani's fixed point theorem (Kakutani [2] ) can be applied after the manner of theorem 5 above to a compact convex subset of an arbitrary locally convex topological linear space. This leads to an extension of the fixed point theorem for multi-valued mappings of Fan [1] and Glicksberg [1] . From a rather special case of that extension, the following fact can be deduced:

8. (Klee [8] ). Let X be a compact Hausdorff space which is an absolute retract for such spaces. Then for each open covering $\alpha$ of X there exists a finite open covering $\beta$ of X which has the following property:

If $f : X \rightarrow X$ is any mapping such that each point $x \in X$ has a neighbourhood U for which $f[U]$ lies in some member of $\beta$ , then there exists a point $x_0 \in X$ such that $x_0$ and $f(x_0)$ lie in the same member of $\alpha$ .

# CHAPTER IV [1)]

## Almost fixed point theorems for the Euclidean plane

DEFINITION. Let X be a topological space, F a family of mappings of X into itself and $\Omega$ a family of finite coverings of X. Then X is said to have the almost fixed point property (a.f.p.p.) with respect to F and $\Omega$ if, for every $f \in F$ and every $\alpha \in \Omega$, there exists a member $U \in \alpha$ such that $U \cap f[U] \neq \emptyset$.

Note that if X is a compact Hausdorff space, then X has the f.p.p. if and only if X has the a.f.p.p. with respect to continuous mappings and finite open coverings.

As was pointed out by Professor J. de Groot, it can be shown that the Euclidean space $E^n$ has the a.f.p.p. with respect to continuous mappings and finite coverings by open sets with compact boundaries. This means that any continuous mapping of $E^n$ into itself either has a fixed point or else there are points far away for which the images also are far away, e.g. a translation.

THEOREM 1. The Euclidean plane $E^2$ has the a.f.p.p. with respect to continuous mappings and finite coverings by convex open sets.

REMARKS. 1. It is easy to see that a corresponding theorem does not hold for infinite (convex open) coverings.

2. It should be possible to generalize theorem 1 by replacing $E^2$ by $E^n$.

We shall use the following lemma (with n=2) in the proof of theorem 1.

LEMMA 1. (Fort [2] ). Let d be a positive number and let $B^n = \{x \in E^n \mid \|x\| < d\}$. Let $f : B^n \to B^n$ be continuous. Then for each $\varepsilon > 0$ there exists a point $x \in B^n$ such that $\|x - f(x)\| < \varepsilon$.

PROOF: Let $\varepsilon > 0$ be given. We may obviously assume that $\varepsilon < d$. Let $C^n = \{x \in B^n \mid \|x\| \leq d - \varepsilon\}$, and define a retraction $r : B^n \to C^n$ by

---------------

1) The results of this chapter will also be published elsewhere (de Groot, de Vries and van der Walt [1] ).

$$r(x) = \begin{cases} (d-\varepsilon)x/\|x\| & \text{for } x \in B^n \setminus C^n, \\ x & \text{for } x \in C^n. \end{cases}$$

Then $rf|C^n: C^n \to C^n$ is continuous and according to the Brouwer fixed point theorem for the n-cell, there exists a point $c \in C^n$ such that $rf(c) = c$. Since $\|r(x)-x\| < \varepsilon$ for all $x \in B^n$, we have $\|c-f(c)\| = \|rf(c)-f(c)\| < \varepsilon$.

DEFINITION. A <u>strip</u> is the closure of an open simply connected set in $E^2$ which is bounded by two parallel straight lines. Let S be a strip bounded by the lines $L_1$ and $L_2$ and let $L_3$ be a (closed) segment, perpendicular to $L_1$ and $L_2$, which connects a point of $L_1$ with a point of $L_2$. Then the closure of a component of $S \setminus L_3$ is called a <u>half-strip</u>. The segment $L_3$ is called the <u>base</u> of the half-strips, and the lines [rays] bounding a strip [half-strip] are called the <u>sides</u> of the strip [half-strip].

It is easy to verify that a convex subset K of $E^2$ with interior points has the following properties:

(i) If $K^o$ (the interior of K) contains a line, then it contains a strip.

(ii) If $K^o$ contains a ray, then it contains a half-strip.

PROOF OF THEOREM 1 : Let $f : E^2 \to E^2$ be a continuous mapping and $\alpha = \{U_i\}_{i=1}^n$ a finite covering of $E^2$ by convex open sets. We may assume that $E^2$ does not belong to $\alpha$. Since $\alpha$ is a finite covering and $E^2$ is unbounded, there exist pairs of different members of $\alpha$ which have unbounded intersections. Such an intersection satisfies either (i) or (ii) above, and we choose, if possible, a strip in each of these intersections; otherwise, we choose a half-strip. Divide each strip in two half-strips, such that the intersection of the ensuing half-strips is their common base. Let $P_1, P_2, \ldots, P_k$ be the collection of half-strips. We may choose them such that $P_i \cap P_j$ $(i \neq j)$ is bounded, and we shall suppose that this was done. Further, we choose an open disk $B_1$ such that the following conditions are fulfilled:

(i) If $U_i \cap U_j$ is bounded, then $\overline{U_i \cap U_j} \subset B_1$ $(i,j=1,2,\ldots,n)$.

(ii) $P_i \cap P_j \subset B_1$ $(i \neq j;\ i,j=1,2,\ldots,k)$.

(iii) The bases of the half-strips as well as the points of intersection of the (prolongations of the) sides of the half-strips are all contained in $B_1$.

Let $B_2$ be an open disk, concentric with $B_1$ and such that $\overline{B}_1 \subset B_2$. We shall now construct a homeomorphism $\varphi : E^2 \to B_2$ such that $\{\varphi[U_i]\}_{i=1}^{n}$ can be extended to an open covering of $\overline{B}_2$.

We shall assume that the collection of half-strips is cyclically ordered by the positive orientation of the boundary of $B_2$, and that this ordering is given by $P_1, P_2, \ldots, P_k$ "modulo k". We also assign an order to the sides of each $P_i$ $(i \equiv 1,2,\ldots,k)$: if we traverse the boundary of $B_2$ in the positive direction, then we pass from the "first side" of $P_i$ to its "second side".

Let $S_i$ denote the closure of that component of $E^2 \setminus (B_1 \cup P_1 \cup \ldots \cup P_k)$ which lies between the second side of $P_i$ and the first side of $P_{i+1}$ $(i \equiv 1,2,\ldots,k)$. $P_i$ and $S_i$ are thus constructed so that there exists a member $U_{j(i)} \in \alpha$ with the property that

(iv) $P_i \cup S_i \cup P_{i+1} \subset U_{j(i)}$ $\quad (i \equiv 1,2,\ldots,k)$.

We are now ready to define the homeomorphism $\varphi : E^2 \to B^2$. It will be done in such a way that $P_i \setminus B_1$ is contracted onto $P_i \cap (B_2 \setminus B_1)$, and $S_i$ onto $S_i \cap (B_2 \setminus B_1)$ $(i \equiv 1,2,\ldots,k)$, while $\overline{B}_1$ is mapped identically onto itself.

<u>$z \in P_i \setminus B_1$ $(i \equiv 1,2,\ldots,k)$</u>: Let $L_i(z)$ be the line through z parallel to the sides of $P_i$, and let $r_i(z) = \text{dist}\,(z, L_i(z) \cap \text{bd}(B_1))$, where $\text{bd}(B_1)$ denotes the boundary of $B_1$. Define $f_i(z)$ to be the point which divides $L_i(z) \cap (B_2 \setminus B_1)$ in the ratio $r_i(z) : 1 + r_i(z)$. It is easy to verify that $f_i$ is a continuous one-to-one mapping of $P_i \setminus B_1$ onto $P_i \cap (B_2 \setminus B_1)$, and that its inverse is continuous.

<u>$z \in S_i$ $(i \equiv 1,2,\ldots,k)$</u>: Let $a_i$ be the point in which the prolongation of the second side of $P_i$ intersects the prolongation of the first side of $P_{i+1}$, and let $\overline{a_i z}$ be the closed segment connecting $a_i$ and z. Let $s_i(z) = \text{dist}(z, \overline{a_i z} \cap \text{bd}(B_1))$, and define $g_i(z)$ to be the point which divides $\overline{a_i z} \cap (B_2 \setminus B_1)$ in the ratio $s_i(z) : 1 + s_i(z)$. Then $g_i$ is a continuous one-to-one mapping of $S_i$ onto $S_i \cap (B_2 \setminus B_1)$, and its inverse is continuous. (If $P_i$ and $P_{i+1}$ are parallel, then we define $g_i$ in the same way as $f_i$ was defined.)

<u>$z \in \overline{B}_1$</u> : Let $h : \overline{B}_1 \to \overline{B}_1$ be the identity mapping.

The functions $f_i, g_i$ and h coincide on the boundaries of their domains of definition and hence $\varphi$, defined by

$$\varphi(z) = \begin{cases} f_i(z) & (z \in P_i \setminus B_1 \ ;\ i \equiv 1,2,\ldots,k), \\ g_i(z) & (z \in S_i;\ i \equiv 1,2,\ldots,k), \\ z & (z \in \overline{B}_1) \end{cases}$$

is a continuous mapping of $E^2$ onto $B_2$. Similarly, $\varphi^{-1}$ is well-defined and continuous; hence $\varphi$ is a homeomorphism.

For each $U_i \in \alpha$, let $U_i' = \varphi[U_i]$ , and let $\varphi(\alpha) = \{U_i'\}_{i=1}^{n}$. For each $U_{j(i)}$ satisfying (iv)(see p.103), let $V_{j(i)} = U'_{j(i)} \cup ((P_i \cup S_i \cup P_{i+1}) \cap \mathrm{bd}(B_2))$. It is easily seen that the $V_{j(i)}$, together with the remaining $U_i'$, form an open covering of $\overline{B}_2$. Denote this covering by $\beta = \{W_i\}_{i=1}^{m}$.

Let $f' = \varphi f \varphi^{-1}$. Then $f' : B_2 \to B_2$ is continuous and according to lemma 1, for each positive integer n, there exists a point $y_n \in B_2$ such that $\|y_n - f'(y_n)\| < \frac{1}{n}$ . Let $\tau$ be the Lebesgue number of $\overline{B}_2$ with respect to $\beta$ , and choose n such that $\frac{1}{n} < \tau$ . According to the lemma of Lebesgue, there exists a set $W_k \in \beta$ such that $y_n$, $f'(y_n) \in W_k$. But $y_n, f'(y_n) \in B_2$, so that $y_n$ and $f'(y_n)$ lie in the same member of $\varphi(\alpha)$. Hence, if $x_n$ is that point of $E^2$ for which $\varphi(x_n) = y_n$, then $x_n$ and $f(x_n)$ lie in the same member of $\alpha$ .

If the mappings are restricted to translations, then we can require less of the covering sets to obtain a theorem similar to theorem 1 : "convex open" may then be replaced by "arcwise connected".

We shall need the following two lemmas.

LEMMA 2. Let $X_1, X_2, \ldots, X_n$ be sets, let $X = \bigcup_{i=1}^{n} X_i$ and let $f : X \to X$ be a mapping. Then there exists a set $X_i$ and a positive number k ($1 \le i, k \le n$) such that $X_i \cap f^k[X_i] \neq \emptyset$.

PROOF: For each $x \in X$, at least two of the n+1 elements x, $f(x), \ldots, f^n(x)$ belong to one and the same set $X_i$; say $f^r(x), f^s(x) \in X_i$ ($1 \le r < s \le n$). Then $f^r(x) \in X_i \cap f^{s-r}[X_i]$ .

LEMMA 3. Let A be an arcwise connected subset of $E^2$, and let $f : E^2 \to E^2$ be a translation, such that there exists a positive integer k with $A \cap f^k[A] \neq \emptyset$. Then $A \cap f[A] \neq \emptyset$ also.

PROOF: Let f be given by $f(x) = x+a$, for all $x \in E^2$, where $a \in E^2$ is a fixed vector. We may suppose that the positive X-axis has the same direction as a. Let k be the smallest positive integer such that $A \cap f^k[A] \neq \emptyset$. Suppose $k > 1$. We are going to derive a contradiction. There exists a point $b \in A$ such that $b+ka \in A$ also, and we can find an arc $J$, contained in $A$, which connects $b$ and $b+ka$. Let

$$P = \{(x,y) \in J \mid (u,v) \in J \Rightarrow y \geq v\} \text{ , and}$$

$$Q = \{(x,y) \in J \mid (u,v) \in J \Rightarrow y \leq v\} \text{ .}$$

Since $J$ is compact, $P \neq \emptyset$ and $Q \neq \emptyset$. ($P$ and $Q$ contain respectively the "upper extreme" and "lower extreme" points of $J$.) Since $J \cap f[J] = \emptyset$, $J$ is not a segment, and since it is compact, we can find a point $p \in P$ and a point $q \in Q$ such that, if $J_1$ is the part of $J$ which connects $p$ and $q$ (including $p$ and $q$), then $J_1 \cap P = \{p\}$, $J_1 \cap Q = \{q\}$, and $p \neq q$.

Let $L_1$ and $L_2$ be straight lines parallel to the X-axis, passing through $p$ and $q$ respectively, and let $S$ be the strip determined by these lines. $J_1$ separates $S$ into two disjoint sets, each of which is simply connected and both open and closed in $S$. The same holds for the images of $J_1$ under the iterates of $f$.

Since $J_1 \cap f[J] = \emptyset$ and $f[J]$ is connected, any two points of $f[J]$, in particular $b+a$ and $q+a$, lie in the same part of $S$ with respect to the separation by $J_1$. Since $f$ is a translation, $b+ka$ and $q+ka$ lie in the same part of $S$ with respect to the separation by $f^{k-1}[J_1]$. Since $q+(k-2)a$ and $q+ka$ lie in different parts of $S$ with respect to this separation, $b+ka$ and $q+(k-2)a$ lie in different parts. Also, $q$ and $q+(k-2)a$ lie in the same part of $S$ with respect to this separation and hence $q$ and $b+ka$ lie in different parts. But $q$ and $b+ka$ are connected by $J$, and $J \subset S$, so that $J \cap f^{k-1}[J_1] \neq \emptyset$, implying that $A \cap f^{k-1}[A] \neq \emptyset$, in contradiction with the choice of $k$.

DEFINITION. Let $X$ be a topological space. Two continuous mappings $f,g : X \to X$ are said to be <u>topologically equivalent</u> if there exists a homeomorphism $h$ of $X$ onto itself such that $f = h^{-1}gh$. If $X$ is a metric space, then a mapping $f : X \to X$ is called a <u>topological isometry</u> if it is topologically equivalent to a distance preserving mapping of $X$ into itself.

In the case of the plane we have the following criterium for a mapping to be a topological translation (Sperner [1] (1934)): A mapping $f : E^2 \to E^2$ is topologically equivalent to a translation if and only if $f$ is an orientation preserving homeomorphism such that, for each set $G \subset E^2$ which is the closure of a bounded domain and whose boundary is a Jordan curve, there exists a positive integer N such that $G \cap f^n[G] = \emptyset$ for all integers n with $|n| \geq N$.

We now state and prove

THEOREM 2. The Euclidean plane has the a.f.p.p. with respect to orientation preserving topological isometries and finite coverings by arcwise connected sets.

PROOF: It is a well-known result that an orientation preserving topological isometry of the Euclidean plane is topologically equivalent either to a rotation or to a translation. In the first case there is a fixed point, and in the second case theorem 2 immediately follows from lemmas 2 and 3.

COROLLARY. The Euclidean plane has the a.f.p.p. with respect to orientation preserving topological isometries and finite coverings by connected open sets.

For, a connected open subset of a Euclidean space is arcwise connected.

An example orally communicated by Professor R.D. Anderson shows that theorem 2 cannot be extended to higher dimensions: There is a covering $\alpha$ of $E^3$ by four non-empty connected open sets, and a topological translation $f : E^3 \longrightarrow E^3$, such that $U \cap f[U] = \emptyset$ for all $U \in \alpha$.

A connected topological space trivially has the a.f.p.p. with respect to arbitrary mappings and coverings consisting of two connected open sets. A unicoherent topological space has the a.f.p.p. with respect to continuous mappings and coverings consisting of three connected open sets. Before showing this, we prove the following

LEMMA 4. Let X be a unicoherent topological space and $\alpha = \{U,V,W\}$ a covering of X by three non-empty connected open sets. Then, if $\cap\alpha = \emptyset$, $\alpha$ has two disjoint members.

PROOF: Suppose, on the contrary, that $U \cap V \neq \emptyset$, $U \cap W \neq \emptyset$ and $V \cap W \neq \emptyset$. Then

$$X = U \cup (V \cup W) \quad \text{(connected summands)}$$
$$U \cap (V \cup W) = (U \cap V) \cup (U \cap W) \quad \text{(connected summands), and}$$
$$(U \cap V) \cap (U \cap W) = U \cap V \cap W = \emptyset,$$

contradicting the unicoherence of X.

THEOREM 3. A unicoherent topological space X has the a.f.p.p. with respect to continuous mappings and coverings consisting of three connected open sets.

PROOF: Let $f : X \to X$ be a continuous mapping and $\alpha = \{U,V,W\}$ a covering of X by three connected open sets. We may suppose that the empty set does not belong to $\alpha$, and that $\cap\,\alpha = \emptyset$. Let U and V be the disjoint members of $\alpha$ given by lemma 4. Then $U \cap W \neq \emptyset$, $V \cap W \neq \emptyset$, since X is connected. Suppose that $W \cap f[W] = \emptyset$. Since $f[W]$ is connected and $U \cap V = \emptyset$, either $f[W] \subset U$ or $f[W] \subset V$. In either case the theorem is proved, e.g. if $f[W] \subset U$, then $f[U \cap W] \subset f[W] \subset U$ and hence $U \cap f[U] \neq \emptyset$.

COROLLARY. $E^n$ has the a.f.p.p. with respect to continuous mappings and coverings consisting of three connected open sets.

For, $E^n$ is unicoherent (Borsuk [2] ).

The question arises whether a unicoherent topological space has the a.f.p.p. with respect to continuous mappings and coverings consisting of four (or more) connected open sets. Further, can "orientation preserving" be omitted from the hypotheses of theorem 2?

Both these questions are answered negatively by the following example, in which we have a covering of $E^2$ by four connected open sets $U_1, U_2, U_3, U_4$, and a transflection f (i.e. a reflection followed by a translation in the direction of the axis of reflection) such that $U_i \cap f[U_i] = \emptyset$ $(i=1,2,3,4)$.

Let

$$V = \{(x,y) \in E^2 \mid 0 < x < 1,\ -1 \leq y < 1\},$$

$$r(x,y) = (x,y) + (2,0), \text{ for all } (x,y) \in E^2,$$

$$s(x,y) = (x,y) + (\tfrac{2}{3},0), \text{ for all } (x,y) \in E^2,$$

$$W = \{(x,y) \in E^2 \mid y < -1\},$$

$$V_1 = \bigcup_{n=-\infty}^{\infty} r^n[V], \quad U_1 = V_1 \cup W,$$

$$U_2 = s[U_1], \quad U_3 = s[U_2],$$

$$U_4 = \{(x,y) \in E^2 \mid y > 0\}.$$

The transflection f is defined as follows:

$$u(x,y) = (x,-y) \text{ for all } (x,y) \in E^2,$$

$$t(x,y) = (x,y) + (1,0) \text{ for all } (x,y) \in E^2,$$

$$f = tu.$$

It is easy to verify that $U_i \cap f[U_i] = \emptyset$ $(i=1,2,3,4)$. Note that f reverses the orientation and that each of the intersections $U_i \cap U_j$ $(i \neq j)$ has countably infinitely many components.

PROBLEMS.

1. Does the Euclidean plane have the a.f.p.p. with respect to orientation preserving homeomorphisms onto and finite coverings by connected open sets?

2. Does the Euclidean plane have the a.f.p.p. with respect to continuous mappings and finite coverings by connected open sets such that the intersection of each pair of members of the covering is empty or has at most a finite number of components?

# BIBLIOGRAPHY


Abian, S.

1. A proof and extension of Brouwer's fixed point theorem for the 2-cell. Boll. Un. Mat. Ital. 16 (1961), 281-284.

Abian, A. (S), and Brown, A.B.

1. A theorem on partially ordered sets, with applications to fixed point theorems. Canad.J. Math. 13 (1961), 78-83.
2. A new fixed point theorem for continuous maps of the closed n-cell. L'Enseignement Mathématique 8 (1962), 33-40.
3. Fixed points of continuous mappings into Euclidean n-space. Duke Math. J. 29 (1962), 647-651.
4. Fixed points and covering under continuous mappings of a spherical shell. Duke Math. J. 29 (1962), 653-655.

Albrecht, R., and Karrer, G.

1. Fixpunktsätze in uniformen Räumen. Math. Zeitschr. 74 (1960), 387-391.

Alexander, J.W.

1. On transformations with invariant points. Trans. Amer. Math. Soc. 23 (1922), 89-95.

Alexandroff, P., and Hopf, H.

1. Topologie I, J. Springer, Berlin, 1935.

Altman, M.

1. A fixed point theorem for completely continuous operators in Banach spaces. Bull. Acad. Polon. Sci. 3 (1955), 409-413.
2. An extension to locally convex spaces of Borsuk's theorem on antipodes. Bull. Acad. Polon. Sci. 6 (1958), 293-295.
3. Continuous transformations of open sets in locally convex spaces. Bull. Acad. Polon. Sci. 6 (1958), 297-301.

Arnold, B.H.

1. A topological proof of the fundamental theorem of algebra. Amer. Math. Month. 56 (1949), 465-466.

Ayres, W.L.

1. Some generalizations of the Scherrer fixed-point theorem. Fund. Math. 16 (1930), 332-336.

Baayen, P.C.

1. Commutatieve transformatie-halfgroepen. Math. Centrum, Amsterdam. Rapport ZW 1963-001.

Banach, S.

1. Théorie des opérations linéaires. Warsaw, 1932.

Begle, E.G.

1. Locally connected spaces and generalized manifolds. Amer. J. Math. 64 (1942), 553-574.
2. The Vietoris mapping theorem for bi-compact spaces. Ann.of Math. 51 (1950), 534-543.
3. A fixed point theorem. Ann.of Math. 51 (1950), 544-550.

Bing, R.H.

1. Concerning hereditarily indecomposable continua. Pacific J. Math. 1 (1951), 43-51.
2. Snake-like continua. Duke Math. J. 18 (1951), 653-663.

Birkhoff, G.

1. Lattice theory (Revised edition). Amer. Math. Soc. Coll. Pub. vol.25, New York, 1948.

Birkhoff, G.D.

1. Proof of Poincaré's geometric theorem. Amer. Math. Soc. Trans. 14 (1913), 14-22.
2. Une généralization à n dimensions du dernier théorème de géométrie de Poincaré. C.R. Acad. Sci. Paris 192 (1931), 196-198.

Birkhoff, G.D., and Kellogg, O.D.

1. Invariant points in function space. Trans. Amer. Math. Soc. 23 (1922), 96-115.

Bohnenblust, H.F.,and Karlin, S.

1. On a theorem of Ville. Contributions to the theory of games, vol. I, 155-160. Annals of Mathematics Studies No.24, Princeton University Press, Princeton, 1950.

Boland, J.Ch.

1. To be published.

Borel, A.

1. Seminar on transformation groups. With contributions by G. Bredon, E.E. Floyd, D. Montgomery, R. Palais. Annals of Mathematics Studies No.46, Princeton University Press, Princeton, 1960.

Borsuk, K.

1. Sur les rétractes. Fund. Math. 17 (1931), 152-170.
2. Quelques théorèmes sur les ensembles unicohérents. Fund. Math. 17 (1931), 171-209.
3. Einige Sätze über stetige Streckenbilder. Fund. Math. 18 (1932), 198-213.
4. Drei Sätze über die n-dimensionale Euklidische Sphäre. Fund. Math. 20 (1933), 177-190.
5. Sur un continu acyclique qui se lasse transformer topologiquement en lui même sans points invariants. Fund.Math.24 (1935), 51-58.
6. Sur un espace compact localement contractible qui n'est pas un rétracte absolu de voisinage. Fund. Math. 35 (1948),175-180.
7. A theorem on fixed points. Bull. Acad. Polon. Sci. 2 (1954), 17-20.

Bosch, J.E.

1. Fixed points of transfinite ordinal operators. Univ.Nac.La Plata Pub. Fac. Ci Fisicomat. Serie Segunda Rev. 5 (1956), 201-214, (1957).

Bourgin, D.G.

1. Classes of transformations and bordering transformations. Bull. Amer. Math. Soc. 57 (1951), 222-237.
2. Un indice dei punti uniti, I, II, III. Atti Acad. Naz.Lincei 19 (1955), 435-440; 20 (1956), 43-48; 21 (1956), 395-400.
3. Fixed points on neighborhood retracts. Revue Math. Pures Appl. 2 Hommage à S. Stoïlow (1957), 371-374.

Brahana, T.R.

1. Products of quasi-complexes. Proc.Amer.Math.Soc.7 (1956), 954-958.

Brodskiĭ, M.S., and Mil'man, D.P.

1. On the center of a convex set. Doklady Akad. Nauk SSSR (N.S.) 59 (1948), 837-840.(Russian) Math.Rev. 9 (1948), 448.

Brouwer, L.E.J.

1. On continuous vector distributions on surfaces. Proc.Kon. Ned.Ak.v.Wet. Ser.A, 11 (1909), 850-858; 12 (1910), 716-734; 13 (1910), 171-186.
2. On continuous one-to-one transformations of surfaces into themselves. Proc.Kon.Ned.Ak.v.Wet. Ser.A, 11 (1909), 788-798; 12 (1910), 286-297; 13 (1911), 767-777; 14 (1911), 300-310; 15 (1913), 352-360; 22 (1920), 811-814; 23 (1921), 232-234.
3. Über Abbildungen von Mannigfaltigkeiten. Math.Ann. 71 (1912), 97-115.
4. Über Jordansche Mannigfaltigkeiten. Math.Ann. 71 (1912), 320-327.
5. Über die periodischen Transformationen der Kugel. Math.Ann. 80 (1919), 39-41.
6. An intuitionist correction of the fixed-point theorem on the sphere. Proc.Roy. London Ser. A 213 (1952), 1-2.

Browder, F.E.

1. The topological fixed point theory and its applications to functional analysis. Princeton Doctoral Thesis, June 1948.
2. On the fixed point index, I, II. Abstracts 319t, 320t, Bull. Amer. Math. Soc. 57 (1951), 280-281.
3. On a generalization of the Schauder fixed point theorem. Duke Math. J. 26 (1959), 291-303.
4. On continuity of fixed points under deformations of continuous mappings. Summa Brasil. Math. 4 (1960), 183-190.
5. On the fixed point index for continuous mappings of locally connected spaces. Summa Brasil. Math. 4 (1960), 253-293.
6. Non-linear functional equations in locally convex spaces. Duke Math. J. 24 (1957), 579-590.

Capel, C.E., and Strother, W.L.

1. A space of subsets having the fixed point property. Proc. Amer.Math. Soc. 7 (1956), 707-708.

2. A theorem of Hamilton: counterexample. Duke Math. J. 24 (1957), 57.

3. Multi-valued functions and partial order. Portugal. Math. 17 (1958), 41-47.

Cartwright, M.L., and Littlewood, J.E.

1. Some fixed point theorems. With appendix by H.D. Ursell. Ann.of Math. 54 (1951), 1-37.

Cesari, L.

1. Existence theorems for periodic solutions of non-linear Lipschitzian differential systems and fixed point theorems. Contributions to the theory of nonlinear oscillations, vol. V, 115-172. Annals of Mathematics Studies No.45, Princeton University Press, Princeton, 1960.

Choquet, G.

1. Points invariants et structure des continus. C.R. Acad.Sci. Paris 212 (1941), 376-379.

Cohen, H.

1. Fixed points in products of ordered spaces. Proc. Amer. Math. Soc. 7 (1956), 703-706.

Connell, E.H.

1. Properties of fixed point spaces. Proc.Amer.Math. Soc. 10 (1959), 974-979.

Dal Saglio, L.

1. Grado topologico e teoremi di esistenza di punti uniti per trasformazioni plurivalenti di 3-celle. Rend.Sem.Mat.Univ. Padova 25 (1956), 386-405.

Darbo, G.

1. Grado topologico e teoremi di esistenza di punti per trasformazioni plurivalenti di bicelle. Rend. Sem. Mat. Univ. Padova 19 (1950), 371-395.

Davis, A.C.

1. A characterization of complete lattices. Pacific J. Math. 5 (1955), 311-319.

Day, M.M.

1. Ergodic theorems for Abelian semigroups. Trans. Amer.Math. Soc. 51 (1942), 399-412.

2. Fixed-point theorems for compact convex sets. Ill.J. Math. 5 (1961), 585-590.

Deleanu, A.

1. Sur un théorème de point fixe. Com. Acad. R.P. Romîne 7 (1957), 839-844. (Rumanian with summaries in Russian and French) Math. Rev. 20 (1959), A 1296.
2. Un théorème de point fixe pour les rétractes des espaces convexoïdes. C.R. Acad. Sci. Paris 247 (1958), 1950-1952.
3. Théorie des points fixed sur les rétractes de voisinage des espaces convexoides. Bull. Soc. Math. France 87 (1959), 235-243.

Dolcher, M.

1. Due teoremi sull 'esistenza di punti uniti nelle trasformazioni piane continue. Rend. Sem. Mat. Univ. Padova 17 (1948), 97-101.

Dugundji, J.

1. An extension of Tietze's theorem. Pacific J. Math. 1 (1951), 353-367.

Dyer, E.

1. The fixed point property on quasi-complexes. Proc. Amer. Math. Soc. Summer Institute on Set Theoretic Topology, Madison, Wisconsin, 1955.
2. A fixed point theorem. Proc. Amer. Math. Soc. 7 (1956), 662-672.

Edelstein, M.

1. An extension of Banach's contraction principle. Proc. Amer. Math. Soc. 12 (1961), 7-10.
2. On fixed and periodic points under contractive mappings. J. London Math. Soc. 37 (1962), 74-79.

Eilenberg, S., and Montgomery, D.

1. Fixed point theorems for multivalued transformations. Amer. J. Math. 68 (1946), 214-222.

Eilenberg, S., and Steenrod, N.

1. Foundations of algebraic topology. Princeton University Press, Princeton, 1952.

Fan, K.

1. Fixed point and minimax theorems in locally convex topological linear spaces. Proc. Nat. Acad. Sci. U.S. 38 (1952), 121-126.
2. A generalization of Tucker's combinatorial lemma with topological applications. Ann. of Math. 56 (1952), 431-437.
3. A generalization of Tychonoff's fixed point theorem. Math. Ann. 142 (1961), 305-310.

Feigl, G.

1. Fixpunktsätze für spezielle n-dimensionale Mannigfaltigkeiten. Math. Ann. 98 (1928), 355-398.

Floyd, E.E.

1. Examples of fixed point sets of periodic maps, I,II. Ann.of Math. 55 (1952), 167-172; 64 (1956), 396-398.
2. On related periodic maps. Amer. J. Math. 74 (1952), 547-554.
3. Fixed point sets of compact Abelian Lie groups of transformations. Ann. of Math. 66 (1957), 30-35.

Fort, M.K., Jr.

1. Essential and non-essential fixed points. Amer. J. Math. 72 (1950), 315-322.
2. Open topological disks in the plane. J. Indian Math. Soc.18 (1954), 23-26.

Franz, W.

1. Abbildungsklassen und Fixpunktklassen drei-dimensionaler Linsenräume. J. Reine Angew. Math. 185 (1943), 65-77.

Fuller, F.B.

1. The homotopy theory of coincidences. Ann. of Math. 59 (1954), 219-226.
2. A relation between degree and linking numbers. Algebraic Geometry and Topology, 258-262. A symposium in honor of S. Lefschetz. Edited by R.H. Fox, D.C. Spencer and A.W. Tucker. Princeton University Press, Princeton,1957.
3. Fixed points of multivalued transformations. Bull. Amer. Math. Soc. 67 (1961), 165-169.

Ginsburg, S.

1. Fixed points of products and ordered sums of simply ordered sets. Proc. Amer. Math. Soc. 5 (1954), 554-565.

Glicksberg, I.L.

1. A further generalization of the Kakutani fixed point theorem, with applications to Nash equilibrium points. Proc. Amer. Math. Soc. 3 (1952), 170-174.

Göhde, D.

1. Über Fixpunktsätze und die Theorie des Abbildungsgrades in Funktionalräumen. Math. Nachr. 20 (1959), 356-371.

Granas, A.

1. Extension homotopy theorem in Banach spaces and some of its applications to the theory of non-linear equations. Bull. Acad. Polon. Sci. 7 (1959), 387-394.
2. An extension to functional spaces of Borsuk-Ulam theorem on antipodes. Bull. Acad. Polon. Sci. 10 (1962), 81-86.

Graves, L.M.

1. Topics in the functional calculus. Bull. Amer. Math. Soc. 41 (1935), 641-662. Errata, ibid 42 (1936), 381-382.

de Groot, J.

1. Groups represented by homeomorphism groups, I. Math. Ann. 138 (1959), 80-102.

de Groot, J., de Vries, H. and van der Walt, T.

1. Almost fixed point theorems for the Euclidean plane. To be published.

Haimo, F.

1. Normal automorphisms and their fixed points. Trans. Amer. Math. Soc. 78 (1955), 150-167.

Halmos, P.R.

1. Measure theory, D. van Nostrand, New York, 1950.

Hamilton, O.H.

1. Fixed points under transformations of continua which are not connected im kleinen. Trans. Amer. Math. Soc. 44 (1938), 18-24.
2. A fixed point theorem for upper semicontinuous transformations on n-cells for which the images of points are non-acyclic continua. Duke Math. J. 14 (1947), 689-693. Correction, ibid 24 (1957), 59.

3. Fixed point theorems for interior transformations. Bull. Amer. Math. Soc. 54 (1948), 383-385.

4. A fixed point theorem for pseudo-arcs and certain other metric continua. Proc. Amer. Math. Soc. 2 (1951), 173-174.

5. Fixed points for certain noncontinuous transformations. Proc. Amer. Math. Soc. 8 (1957), 750-756.

Hammond Smith, D.

1. Hyperspaces of a CANR*. Proc. Cambridge Philos. Soc. 57 (1961), 754-758.

Hamstrom, M.-E.

1. Some global properties of homeomorphisms on a disc with holes. Duke Math. J. 29 (1962), 657-662.

Hedrlín, Z.

1. On common fixed points of commutative mappings. Comm. Math. Univ. Car. (2) 4 (1961), 25-28.

2. On commutativity of transformations. Math. Centrum, Amsterdam. Rapport ZW 1962-015.

3. On a common fixed point of a commutative semigroup of continuous mappings. Math. Centrum, Amsterdam. Rapport ZW 1962-024.

Hopf, H.

1. Über die algebraische Anzahl von Fixpunkten. Math. Zeitschr. 29 (1929), 493-524.

2. Freie Überdeckungen und freie Abbildungen, Fund. Math. 28 (1937), 33-57.

Hukuhara, M.

1. Sur l'existence des points invariants d'une transformation dans l'espace fonctionnel. Jap. J. Math. 20 (1950), 1-4.

Inaba, M.

1. A theorem on fixed points and its application to the theory of differential equations. Kumamoto J. Sci. Ser. A 1 (1952), 13-16.

Isbell, J.R.

1. Commuting mappings of trees. Research Problem 7, Bull. Amer. Math. Soc. 63 (1957), 419.

Jaworowski, J.W.

1. Theorem on antipodes for multivalued mappings and a fixed point theorem. Bull. Acad. Polon. Sci. 4 (1956), 187-192.

Kakutani, S.

1. Two fixed-point theorems concerning bicompact convex sets. Proc. Imp. Acad. Jap. 14 (1938), 242-245.
2. A generalization of Brouwer's fixed point theorem. Duke Math. J. 8 (1941), 457-459.
3. A proof that there exists a circumscribing cube around any bounded closed convex set in $R^3$. Ann. of Math. 43 (1942), 739-741.
4. Topological properties of the unit sphere of Hilbert space. Proc. Imp. Acad. Tokyo 19 (1943), 269-271.

Kantorovitch, L.

1. The method of successive approximations for functional equations. Acta Math. 71 (1939), 63-97.

Kelley, J.L.

1. Fixed sets under homeomorphisms. Duke Math. J. 5 (1939), 535-537.
2. A decomposition of compact continua and related theorems on fixed sets under continuous transformations. Proc.Nat. Acad. Sci. U.S.A. 26 (1940), 192-194.
3. Hyperspaces of a continuum. Trans. Amer. Math. Soc. 52 (1942), 22-36.
4. General topology. D. van Nostrand, New York, 1955.

Kerékjártó, B. von.

1. Über Transformationen des ebenen Kreisringes. Math. Ann. 80 (1921), 33-35.
2. Vorlesungen über Topologie I. J. Springer, Berlin, 1923.

Kinoshita, S.

1. On essential components of the set of fixed points. Osaka Math. J. 4 (1952), 19-22.
2. On some contractible continua without fixed point property. Fund. Math. 40 (1953), 96-98.

Klee, V.L., Jr.

1. Convex bodies and periodic homeomorphisms in Hilbert space. Trans. Amer. Math. Soc. 74 (1953), 10-43.

2. Some topological properties of convex sets. Trans. Amer. Math. Soc. 78 (1955), 30-45.
3. Fixed-point sets of periodic homeomorphisms of Hilbert space. Ann. of Math. 64 (1956), 393-395.
4. A note on topological properties of normed linear spaces. Proc. Amer. Math. Soc. 7 (1956), 673-674.
5. An example related to the fixed-point property. Nieuw Arch. Wisk. 8 (1960), 81-82.
6. Shrinkable neighborhoods in Hausdorff linear spaces. Math. Ann. 141 (1960), 281-285.
7. Leray-Schauder theory without local convexity. Math. Ann. 141 (1960), 286-296.
8. Stability of the fixed-point property. Colloq. Math. 8 (1961), 43-46.
9. Personal communication.
10. Personal communication.

Knaster, B.

1. Un théorème sur les fonctions d'ensembles. Ann. Soc. Polon. Math. 6 (1928), 133-134.

Knaster, B., Kuratowski, K., and Mazurkiewicz, S.

1. Ein Beweis des Fixpunktsatzes für n-dimensionale Simplexe. Fund. Math. 14 (1929), 132-137.

Krasnosel'skiĭ, M.A.

1. On a fixed point principle for completely continuous operators in functional spaces. Doklady Akad. Nauk SSSR(N.S.) 73 (1950), 13-15. (Russian) Math. Rev. 12 (1951), 111.
2. On the theory of completely continuous vector fields. Ukrain. Mat. Žurnal 3 (1951), 174-183. (Russian)Math. Rev. 14 (1953), 1109.
3. Fixed points of cone compressing or cone-extending operators. Sov. Math. Dokl. 1 (1960), 1285-1288. Russian original: Dokl. Akad. Nauk. SSSR 135.

Krein, M.,and Šmulian, V.

1. Regularly convex sets. Ann. of Math. 41 (1940), 556-583.

Kyner, W.T.

1. A fixed point theorem. Contributions to the theory of nonlinear oscillations, vol.III, 197-205. Annals of Mathematics Studies No.36, Princeton University Press, Princeton, 1956.

2. Small periodic perturbations of an autonomous system of vector equations. Contributions to the theory of nonlinear oscillations, vol. IV, 111-124. Annals of Mathematics Studies No. 41, Princeton University Press, Princeton, 1958.

Lefschetz, S.

1. Intersections and transformations of complexes and manifolds. Trans. Amer. Math. Soc. 28 (1926), 1-49.
2. Manifolds with a boundary and their transformations. Trans. Amer. Math. Soc. 29 (1927), 429-462.
3. Topology. Amer. Math. Soc. Coll. Pub. vol.12 New York,1930.
4. On the fixed point formula. Ann. of Math. 38 (1937), 819-822.
5. Algebraic topology. Amer. Math. Soc. Coll. Pub. vol.27, New York, 1942.
6. Topics in topology. Annals of Mathematics Studies No.10, Princeton University Press, Princeton, 1942.
7. Introduction to topology. Princeton University Press, Princeton, 1949.
8. On coincidences of transformations. Boll. Soc. Mat. Mexicana 2 (1957), 16-25.

Leray, J.

1. Topologie des espaces de Banach. C.R. Acad. Sci. Paris 200 (1935), 1082-1084.
2. Sur la forme des espaces topologiques et sur les points fixes des représentations. J.Math. Pures Appl. 24 (1945), 95-167.
3. Sur la position d'un ensemble fermé de points d'un espace topologique. J.Math. Pures Appl. 24 (1945), 169-199.
4. Sur les équations et les transformations. J.Math. Pures Appl. 24 (1945), 201-248.
5. La théorie des points fixes et ses applications en analyse. Proc. Int. Congr. Math. (1950), Cambridge, Massachusetts, vol. 2, 202-208.
6. Théorie des points fixes, indice total et nombre de Lefschetz. Bull. Soc. Math. France 87 (1959), 221-233.

Leray, J., and Schauder, J.

1. Topologie et équations fonctionelles. Ann.Sci. École Norm. Sup. 51 (1934), 45-78.

Lusternik, L., and Schnirelmann, L.

1. Méthodes topologiques dans les problèmes variationnels. (Russian). See Jahrb. Fortschr. Math. 56 (1930), 1134.

Luxemburg, W.A.J.

1. On the convergence of successive approximations in the theory of ordinary differential equations, II. Proc. Kon. Ned. Ak.v. Wet. Ser. A 61 (1958), Indag. Math. 20 (1958), 540-546.

Magenes, E.

1. Un criterio di esistenza di punti uniti in trasformazioni topologiche piane. Rend. Sem. Mat. Univ. Padova 18 (1949), 68-114.
2. Un' osservazione sui teoremi di esistenza di punti uniti in trasformazioni plurivalenti di una N-cella. Rend. Sem. Mat. Univ. Padova 19 (1950), 108-113.

Markov, A.A.

1. Quelques théorèmes sur les ensembles abéliens. Doklady Akad. Nauk SSSR (N.S.) 10 (1936), 311-314.

Marcus, M.D.

1. An invariant surface theorem for a non-degenerate system. Contributions to the theory of nonlinear oscillations, vol. III, 243-256. Annals of Mathematics Studies No.36, Princeton University Press, Princeton, 1956.
2. Repeating solutions for a degenerate system. Ibid., 261-268.

Maxwell, C.N.

1. Fixed points of symmetric product mappings. Proc.Amer.Math. Soc. 8 (1957), 808-815.

Mazur, S.

1. Über die kleinste konvexe Menge , die eine gegebene kompakte Menge enthält. Studia Math. 2 (1930), 7-9.

Mioduszewski, J., and Rochowski, M.

1. Remarks on fixed point theorem for inverse limit spaces. Proceedings of the Symposium on General Topology and its relation to Modern Analysis and Algebra, 275-276. Publishing House of the Czechoslovak Academy of Sciences, Prague, 1962.

Miranda, C.

1. Problemi di esistenza in analisi funzionale. Scuola Normale Superiore, Pisa. Quaderni Matematica, No.3. Litografia Tacchi, Pisa, 1950.

Monna, A.F.

1. Sur un théorème de M. Luxemburg les points fixes d'une classe d'applications d'un espace métric dans lui-même. Proc.Kon.Ned.Ak.v.Wet. Ser.A 64 (1961), Indag.Math. 23 (1961), 89-96.

Myškis, A.D.

1. Generalizations of the theorem on a fixed point of a dynamical system inside of a closed trajectory. Mat. Sbornik N.S. 34 (76) (1954), 525-540. (Russian) Math. Rev. 15 (1954), 978.

Nagumo, M.

1. Degree of mapping of manifolds based on that of Euclidean open sets. Osaka Math. J. 2 (1950), 105-118.
2. Degree of mappings in convex linear topological spaces. Amer. J. Math. 73 (1951), 497-511.

Nash, J.

1. Generalized Brouwer theorem. Research Problem, Bull. Amer. Math. Soc. 62 (1956), 76.

Nemyčkiǐ, V.

1. The methods of fixed points in analysis. Uspehi Matem.Nauk 1 (1936), 141-174.(Russian)

Newman, M.H.A.

1. Fixed point and coincidence theorems. J. London Math. Soc. 27 (1952), 135-140.

Nielsen, J.

1. Untersuchungen zur Topologie des geschlossen zweiseitigen Flache, I,II,III. Acta Math. 50 (1927), 189-358; 53 (1929), 1-76; 58 (1932), 87-167.

Nöbeling, G.

1. Eine Fixpunkteigenschaft der Baumkurven. Ergebnisse eines math. Kolloquiums 2 (1932), 19.

O'Neill, B.

1. Essential sets and fixed points. Amer.J. Math. 75 (1953), 497-509.
2. A fixed point theorem for multi-valued functions. Duke Math. J. 24 (1957), 61-62.
3. Induced homology homomorphisms for set-valued maps. Pacific J. Math. 7 (1957), 1179-1184.

Plunkett, R.L.

1. A fixed point theorem for continuous multi-valued transformations. Proc.Amer. Math. Soc. 7 (1956), 160-163.

Pelczar, A.

1. On the invariant points of a transformation. Ann.Polon.Math. 11 (1961), 199-202.

Poincaré, H.

1. Sur les courbes definies par une équation différentielle, III. J.Math. Pures Appl. (C. Jordan) 1 (1885), 167-244.

Reifenberg, E.R.

1. Fixed points on rotating continua. Proc. Cambridge Philos. Soc. 50 (1954), 1-7.

Rey Pastor, J.

1. The last geometric theorems of Poincaré and their applications. Union Mat. Argentina. Memorias y Monografias (2) 1 No.4 (1945), 42 pp. (Spanish, French summary) Math. Rev. 7 (1946), 471.

Rosen, R.H.

1. Fixed points for multivalued functions on snake-like continua. Proc. Amer. Math. Soc. 10 (1959), 167-173.

Rothe, E.H.

1. Uber Abbildungsklassen von Kugeln des Hilbertschen Raumes. Compositio Math. 4 (1937), 294-307.
2. Uber den Abbildungsgrad bei Abbildungen von Kugeln des Hilbertschen Raumes. Compositio Math. 5 (1938), 166-176.
3. Zur Theorie der topologischen Ordnung und der Vektorfelder in Banachschen Räumen. Compositio Math. 5 (1938), 177-197.
4. The theory of topological order in some linear topological spaces. Iowa State College J. Sci. 13 (1939), 373-390.

5. Topological proofs of uniqueness theorems in the theory of differential and integral equations. Bull. Amer. Math. Soc. 45 (1939), 606-613.

Schauder, J.

1. Zur Theorie stetiger Abbildungen in Funktionalräumen. Math. Zeitschr. 26 (1927), 47-65; 417-431.
2. Der Fixpunktsatz in Funktionalraum. Studia Math. 2 (1930), 171-180.

Scherrer, W.

1. Über ungeschlossene stetige Kurven. Math. Zeitschr. 24 (1926), 125-130.

Schweigert, G.E.

1. Fixed elements and periodic types for homeomorphisms on s.l.c. continua. Amer. J. Math. 66 (1944), 229-244.

Scorza Dragoni, G.

1. Un 'osservazione sull'esistenza di elementi uniti nelle trasformazioni topologiche del cerchio. Ann. Mat. Pura Appl. 19 (1940), 45-49.
2. Criteri per l'esistenza di punti uniti in trasformazioni topologiche del cerchio e loro applicazioni. Ann.Mat. Pura Appl. 25 (1946), 43-65.

Segal, J.

1. A fixed point theorem for the hyperspace of a snake-like continuum. Fund. Math. 50 (1962), 237-248.

Smith, P.A.

1. Fixed points of periodic transformations. Appendix B of Lefschetz [5] , 1942.
2. New results and old problems in finite transformation groups. Bull. Amer. Math. Soc. 66 (1960), 402-415.

Sperner, E.

1. Über die fixpunktfreien Abbildungen der Ebene. Abh. Math. Sem. Ham. Univ. 10 (1934), 1-47.

Stallings, J.

1. Fixed point theorems for connectivity maps. Fund.Math. 47 (1959), 249-263.

Steenrod, N.E.

1. Universal homology groups. Amer.J. Math. 58 (1936), 661-701.

Stokes, A.P.

1. The applications of a fixed point theorem to a variety of nonlinear stability problems. Contributions to the theory of nonlinear oscillations, vol. V, 173-184. Annals of Mathematics Studies No.45, Princeton University Press, Princeton, 1960.

Strother, W.L.

1. On an open question concerning fixed points. Proc. Amer. Math. Soc. 4 (1953), 988-993.
2. Fixed points, fixed sets and M-retracts. Duke Math. J. 22 (1955), 551-556.

Strother, W.L. and Ward, L.E., Jr.

1. Retracts from neighborhood retracts. Duke Math.J. 25 (1957), 11-14.

Swan, R.G.

1. A new method in fixed point theory. Comment. Math. Helv. 34 (1960), 1-16.

Tarski, A.

1. A lattice-theoretical fixpoint theorem and its applications. Pacific J. Math. 5 (1955), 285-309.

Trevisan, G.

1. Punti uniti in trasformazioni del cerchio. Giorn. Mat. Battaglini 3 (79) (1950), 127-131.

Tuckey, J.W.

1. Convergence and uniformity in topology. Annals of Mathematics Studies No.2, Princeton University Press, Princeton, 1940.

Tychonoff, A.

1. Ein Fixpunktsatz. Math. Ann. 111 (1935), 767-776.

Verčenko, L.

1. Sur les continus acycliques transformés en eux-mêmes d'une manière continue sans points invariants. Rec. Math. [Math. Sbornik] N.S. 8 (50) (1940), 295-306. (Russian. French summary) Math. Rev. 2 (1941), 324.

Vietoris, L.

1. Über den höheren Zusammenhang kompakter Räume und eine Klasse von zusammenhangstreun Abbildungen. Math. Ann. 97 (1927), 454-472.

Volpato, M.

1. Un criterio per l'esistenza di elementi uniti nelle trasformazioni topologiche del cerchio. Atti Acad. Naz. Lincei. Rend. Cl. Sci. Fis. Mat. Nat. 1 (1946), 704-709.
2. Sull 'esistenza di punti uniti nelle trasformazioni univoche e continue del cerchio. Ann. Mat. Pura Appl. 27 (1948), 101-105.

Wallace, A.D.

1. A fixed point theorem for trees. Bull. Amer. Math. Soc. 47 (1941), 757-760.
2. A fixed-point theorem. Bull. Amer. Math. Soc. 51 (1945), 413-416.
3. Group invariant continua. Fund. Math. 36 (1949), 119-124.

Wang, H.

1. A remark on transformation groups leaving fixed an end point. Proc. Amer. Math. Soc. 3 (1952), 548-549.

Ward, L.E., Jr.

1. Partially ordered topological spaces. Proc. Amer. Math.Soc. 5 (1954), 144-161.
2. A note on dendrites and trees. Proc. Amer. Math. Soc. 5 (1954), 992-994.
3. Continua invariant under monotone transformations. J. London Math. Soc. 31 (1956), 114-119.
4. Mobs, trees, and fixed points. Proc. Amer. Math. Soc.8 (1957), 798-804.
5. Completeness in semi-lattices. Canad.J. Math. 9 (1957), 578-582.
6. A fixed point theorem. Amer.Math. Monthly 65 (1958), 271-272.
7. A fixed point theorem for multivalued functions. Pacific J. Math. 8 (1958), 921-927.
8. A fixed point theorem for chained spaces. Pacific J. Math. 9 (1959), 1273-1278.

9. Characterization of the f.p.p. for a class of set-valued mappings. Fund. Math. 50 (1961), 159-164.

10. Fixed point theorems for pseudo monotone mappings. Proc. Amer. Math. Soc. 13 (1962), 13-16.

Wecken, F.

1. Fixpunktklassen, I,II,III. Math.Ann. 117 (1941), 659-671; 118 (1942), 216-234; 118 (1942), 544-577.

Weier, J.

1. On plane vector fields. Math. Japon. 3 (1955), 163-172.
2. Über Transformation von Kompakten in die Sphäre. Proc.Japan. Acad. 35 (1959), 599-602.

Wilder, R.L.

1. Topology of manifolds. Amer. Math. Soc. Coll. Pub., vol.32, New York, 1949 .
2. Some mapping theorems with applications to non-locally connected spaces. Algebraic Geometry and Topology, 378-388. A symposium in honor of S. Lefschetz. Edited by R.H. Fox, D.C. Spencer and A.W. Tucker, Princeton University Press, Princeton, 1957.

Wolk, E.S.

1. Dedekind completeness and a fixed point theorem. Canad.J. Math. 9 (1957), 400-405.

Yang, C.T.

1. On theorems of Borsuk-Ulam, Kakutani-Yamabe-Yujobô and Dyson, I,II. Ann. of Math. 60 (1954), 262-282; 62 (1955), 271-283.
2. Continuous functions from spheres to Euclidean spaces. Ann.of Math. 62 (1955), 284-291.

Yood, B.

1. On fixed points for semi-groups of linear operators. Proc. Amer. Math. Soc. 2 (1951), 225-233.

Young, G.S.

1. The introduction of local connectivity by change of topology. Amer.J. Math. 68 (1946), 479-494.
2. Fixed-point theorems for arcwise connected continua. Proc. Amer. Math. Soc. 11 (1960), 880-884.

Zeeman, E.C.

1. The topology of the brain and visual perception. Topology of 3-manifolds and related topics, 240-256. Edited by M.K. Fort, Prentice Hall, Inc., Englewood Cliffs, N.J., 1962.

Added in print:

Dunford, N., and Schwartz, J.T.

1. Linear Operators, I. Interscience Pub., New York, 1953.

Kuratowski, C.

1. Topologie, I,II. Monografie Matematyczne, Warszawa, 1952 and 1961.

Whyburn, G.T.

1. Analytic topology. Amer.Math.Soc. Coll. Publ. vol.28, New York, 1942.